Transport Technology for Developing Regions:
A Study of Road Transportation in Venezuela

Richard M. Soberman

The M.I.T. Press
Massachusetts Institute of Technology
Cambridge, Massachusetts, and London, England

VENEZUELA
POLITICAL AND PHYSICAL

4-65
N Dis.

BEAN   SEA

NUEVA
ESPARTA
Juan
Griego   LA ASUNCION

Carúpano

TRINIDAD

CUMANÁ   S U C R E   GULF   OF
PARIA

NDA
Pto. la Cruz
BARCELONA
Naricual   Caripito

MATURIN

Aragua de
Barcelona   Anaco   R. Guanipa
Cantaura   M O N A G A S   TUCUPITA

Valle de
la Pascua   San Tomé   Barrancas
El Tigre   El Tigrito

I C O   Pto. Ord.   San Félix   TERRITORIO   FEDERAL
DELTA   AMACURO
El Pao
Upata

CIUDAD
BOLIVAR   Río

RIO   ORINOCO   Caroni

Cerro
Bolívar   Altamira
Cd. Piar   Rondón

Río Caura

BRITISH

GUIANA

B   O   L   I   V   A   R

LA   GRAN

SABANA

Río

Río

Paragua

DERAL

AMAZONAS   B   R   A   Z   I   L

B

13/4

EDINBURGH UNIVERSITY LIBRARY

Transport Technology for Developing Regions

A Publication of the Joint Center for Urban Studies
of the Massachusetts Institute of Technology
and Harvard University

This monograph is one of a series published under the auspices of the Joint Center for Urban Studies, a cooperative venture of the Massachusetts Institute of Technology and Harvard University. The Joint Center was founded in 1959 to organize and encourage research on urban and regional problems. Participants have included scholars from the fields of anthropology, architecture, business, city planning, economics, education, engineering, history, law, philosophy, political science, and sociology.

The findings and conclusions of this monograph are, as with all Joint Center publications, solely the responsibility of the author.

Other books published in the Joint Center series include:

CHARLES ABRAMS, *Man's Struggle for Shelter in an Urbanizing World.* The M.I.T. Press, 1964.

WILLIAM ALONSO, *Location and Land Use.* Harvard University Press, 1964.

MARTIN ANDERSON, *The Federal Bulldozer.* The M.I.T. Press, 1964.

DONALD APPLEYARD, KEVIN LYNCH, and JOHN R. MYER, *The View from the Road.* The M.I.T. Press, 1964.

EDWARD C. BANFIELD and JAMES Q. WILSON, *City Politics.* Harvard University Press, 1963.

JOHN E. BURCHARD and OSCAR HANDLIN, editors, *The Historian and the City.* The M.I.T. Press, 1963.

RALPH W. CONANT, editor, *The Public Library and the City.* The M.I.T. Press, 1965.

BERNARD J. FRIEDEN, *The Future of Old Neighborhoods.* The M.I.T. Press, 1964.

JOHN FRIEDMANN, *Regional Development Policy: A Case Study of Venezuela.* The M.I.T. Press, 1966.

NATHAN GLAZER and DANIEL P. MOYNIHAN, *Beyond the Melting Pot.* The M.I.T. Press, 1963.

CHARLES HAAR, *Law and Land: Anglo-American Planning Practice.* Harvard University Press, 1964.

KEVIN LYNCH, *The Image of the City.* The M.I.T. Press, 1960.

MARTIN MEYERSON and EDWARD C. BANFIELD, *Boston: The Job Ahead.* Harvard University Press, 1966.

LLOYD RODWIN, *Housing and Economic Progress.* The M.I.T. Press, 1961.

STEPHAN THERNSTROM, *Poverty and Progress.* Harvard University Press, 1964.

RAYMOND VERNON, *The Myth and Reality of Our Urban Problems.* Harvard University Press, 1966.

SAM B. WARNER, JR., *Streetcar Suburbs.* Harvard University Press, 1962.

MORTON AND LUCIA WHITE, *The Intellectual Versus the City: From Thomas Jefferson to Frank Lloyd Wright.* Harvard University Press, 1962.

JAMES Q. WILSON, editor, *Urban Renewal: The Record and the Controversy.* The M.I.T. Press, 1966.

FOREWORD

In 1961, the Joint Center for Urban Studies of M.I.T. and Harvard was given a unique opportunity to participate in the planning of a new city in the interior of Venezuela at the confluence of the Orinoco and Caroní rivers. The city, Ciudad Guayana, was being developed by the Corporación Venezolana de Guayana (CVG), a semiautonomous Venezuelan government agency charged with exploiting the great natural resources of the region—principally hydroelectric power and iron ore. The administration of President Romulo Betancourt decided not only to take advantage of these resources but in addition to provide coordinated development for the entire region around the new city so as to ensure balanced industrial growth and, above all, the creation of a metropolis that would preserve the natural beauties of the site, supply the facilities for sound community life, and minimize the hardships that inevitably attend rapid population growth in a developing country.

For five years, a group of physical planners, economists, urban designers, lawyers, anthropologists, and others recruited by the Joint Center worked as colleagues of the CVG's professional staff in meeting emergencies, assessing alternative strategies, and formulating goals and priorities. The Guayana Project staff of the Joint Center was supplemented during the summers and at other times with faculty and students from M.I.T., Harvard, and elsewhere. These scholars not only had the task of providing advice and assistance to the Project on matters of special importance but were also expected to carry out studies that would contribute to our understanding of the fundamental problems of urban and regional growth, and of the ways in which planners can and cannot cope with those problems and assist persons undertaking regional development programs elsewhere. The hope was that the Joint Center could serve not only its client but the teaching and research interests of its two parent universities as well.

Whatever success we had in meeting these dual—and occasionally conflicting—objectives was due in no small part to the imagination, competence, and forbearance of the CVG and especially of its President, General Rafael Alfonso Ravard. The work of the Joint Center in the Guayana was paid for entirely by funds of the Venezuelan government. The CVG allowed the Joint Center to set aside, out of its budget for this project, a special budget to finance scholarly studies of the project, even though some of these studies were primarily of intellectual interest to the Joint Center rather than of practical value to the CVG. We wish to record our gratitude to the CVG and to the Venezuelan government for not only permitting, but also encouraging, this experiment in combining the functions of adviser and scholar.

This book is one of a series written by men and women who participated in the Guayana Project, either as full-time members of the professional advisory staff, or as professors or graduate students who served as summer consultants to the staff, or as researchers attached to the Project. In practice, it was, of course, impossible to maintain rigid distinctions between those who were in Guayana to "advise" and those who were there to "do research." The latter group inevitably found itself drawn into discussions, and even decisions, about a wide range of issues. Happily, no researcher was so bloodless as to refuse this challenge or so weak as to lose his objectivity as a result.

This book series is not intended to be a history of the project or a record of the decisions made there. Each volume is a separate monograph on a subject of intrinsic intellectual interest, written for other scholars and practitioners working in similar fields, and published because it meets the normal requirements of scholarship by which the Joint Center and the M.I.T. and Harvard presses judge all their manuscripts. What these books have in common is that, whatever their subject, the data were drawn in whole or in part from the Venezuela project. A forthcoming volume in this series, edited by Lloyd Rodwin (who had general responsibility for the direction of the Guayana Project as well as serving as Chairman of the Faculty Committee of the Joint Center), is intended to give the general reader an overview of all aspects of the Project.

The first volume in this series was *Regional Development Policy: A Case Study of Venezuela,* by John Friedmann. This book by Richard M. Soberman is the second. Professor Soberman was, at the time he carried out this research, a graduate student in civil engineering at M.I.T., and the manuscript was originally written as his doctoral thesis. While serving with the Guayana Project, he, like so many other researchers, prepared various staff papers—in this case on transportation planning in the region. The book has been reviewed by both the CVG and the Joint Center, but the contents are entirely the responsibility of the author. Mr. Soberman was free to accept or reject any suggestions made to him by the CVG as to the contents of the book.

Subsequent books in this series will include studies of migration to the region, daily life in a *barrio* of the city, economic planning, education in a developing country, and other subjects.

James Q. Wilson
Director, Joint Center for Urban Studies

Lloyd Rodwin
Chairman of the Faculty Committee,
Joint Center for Urban Studies

PREFACE

This book is intended primarily as a guide for engineers working on transportation problems in underdeveloped regions. Its purpose is to point out how various economic concepts can be incorporated into engineering design. No attempt is made to contribute to the already expanding literature on these subjects *per se*. Therefore, although economists may find the subject matter of interest they should not expect to find a great deal in the way of economic sophistication in some of the discussions. In some respects, the maxim that "a little knowledge is a dangerous thing" has been disregarded in the belief that some exposure to economics, even in the most rudimentary manner, cannot help but influence engineers to ask more of the relevant questions in evaluating alternative transportation proposals in underdeveloped countries.

In 1961, the Joint Center for Urban Studies of the Massachusetts Institute of Technology and Harvard University undertook to assist the Corporación Venezolana de Guayana in planning for the economic development of the Guayana region of Venezuela. This book is based largely on a doctoral dissertation prepared at the Massachusetts Institute of Technology after having been associated with this project as a research fellow for a period of one year. I am grateful both for the financial assistance provided by the Corporación Venezolana de Guayana through the Joint Center for Urban Studies and for the opportunity to write a dissertation under circumstances that most doctoral candidates would find enviable.

The analytical work is based largely on empirical data collected in Venezuela, much of which would have been difficult to obtain without the assistance of Alexander Ganz, Chief Economist for the Joint Center-Guayana Project, and Roberto Alamo Blanco, Head of the Economic Planning Division, Corporación Venezolana de Guayana. The assistance of Antonio Ablan, R. Gil Duarte, Teodoro Gathman, José Gonzales Lander, and Llewelyn Thatcher of the Ministerio de Obras Publicas (Ministry of Public Works) in Caracas is also gratefully acknowledged.

Appreciative credit goes to the International Bank for Reconstruction and Development for supplying the map of Venezuela used as end pages for this volume. The map first appeared in *The Economic Development of Venezuela,* The Johns Hopkins Press, 1960.

I would particularly like to express my appreciation to Blair T. Bower, who painstakingly commented on various drafts of the manuscript, and to Antonio Boccalandro, who was most helpful in indicating the best sources of data and in continually forcing me to test the practicability of the theoretical developments. The thoughtful comments of Alexander J. Bone, Aaron Fleisher, Robert H. Jones, Louis Lefeber, John R. Meyer, Martin Meyerson, Lloyd Rodwin, and Martin Wohl are also acknowledged. The responsibility for any errors or omissions is, of course, entirely my own.

I am grateful to my wife, Marilyn, for typing the early drafts of this manuscript and checking many of the computations, as well as for her encouragement and for many holidays forgone. The assistance of Mrs. Joy White in typing the final draft is also appreciated.

A great deal of what the reader may find worth while in this book can indirectly be traced back to A. Scheffer Lang, formerly Assistant Professor of Transportation Engineering at the Massachusetts Institute of Technology.

RICHARD M. SOBERMAN
University of Toronto
October 1965

CONTENTS

CONTENTS

Transport Technology for Developing Regions

A Publication of the Joint Center for Urban Studies
of the Massachusetts Institute of Technology
and Harvard University

INTRODUCTION

Transportation problems in developing regions of the world are receiving increasingly more attention from economists, engineers, and regional planners. In planning for the development of most regions, the question usually arises as to what role transportation is to play. Generally, planners tend to attach considerable weight to the availability of adequate transportation facilities—to the extent that transportation is often credited with initiating development by itself. References to the role of the transcontinental railroads in opening the North American West are endlessly cited in reports dealing with the justification of large-scale transportation projects in developing regions.

There is little doubt, of course, that transportation or the lack of it can be an important factor in regional development. The role of transportation, however, is primarily a permissive one, the existence of adequate transport capacity being a necessary but not sufficient condition for stimulating economic activity. Generally, where the development effects of improvements in transport have been dramatic, the means of development already existed and the lack of adequate transportation was the one factor restraining development. In such cases private investors have often shown themselves willing and able to provide the necessary means of transportation.

The extent to which transportation problems of underdeveloped regions differ from those of more economically advanced regions depends largely on the relative importance attached to the various consequences of a decision to invest in a transportation facility. Such consequences are of two types—those that

1

directly affect the users of the facility and those that indirectly affect nonusers. Both types of consequences may be either economic or quasi-economic in character. Examples of strictly economic consequences include the costs of constructing, operating, and maintaining the transportation facility. Quasi-economic consequences include savings in user time, comfort, convenience, safety, and general effects on health, education, and welfare.

In well-developed economies, strictly economic consequences such as user costs are often of secondary importance to quasi-economic consequences such as time and safety. The latter are likely to have less importance in underdeveloped regions.[1] On the other hand, the relative importance of indirect consequences is likely to be greater in underdeveloped economies. Highly developed economies are usually characterized by dense transport networks; thus, relatively speaking, the effect of one new addition to the transport system on the entire economy is likely to be less than in underdeveloped economies where one transport link may mean the difference between undercapacity and overcapitalization in the transport sector. In addition, where the transport network is less dense, the effects of transport improvements on expanding the area of influence of the few welfare facilities that do exist is generally more pronounced. In other words, indirect consequences are likely to be relatively more important. Because these indirect consequences are not usually expressable in commensurable terms, the usefulness of traditional marginal benefit-cost analysis for evaluating alternative transportation proposals in such regions is seriously limited.

Planning a complete system of regional transportation involves specification both of the types of transport facilities re-

---

[1] The utility of time is closely related to the income of the user. Since, by definition, average incomes in underdeveloped regions are less than in developed economies, the average value attached to user time savings should also be lower. Philosophically, it might be argued that the income distribution in an underdeveloped economy may be such that average incomes of users are higher than in developed countries and that time savings ought therefore be valued more highly. There appears to be little evidence to support this contention, however.

quired and of the time at which such facilities should become available. In particular, a regional plan for transportation should specify:

a. The location of transport routes in space.

b. The physical description of these routes in terms of their type and standards.

c. The scheduling of investments in the transportation system over future time periods.

d. Methods of financing construction of the transportation system.

e. Methods of operating and maintaining the completed system.

f. The pricing policy to be employed in charging for transport services provided by the system.

Three steps are usually involved in this procedure. First, an accurate determination of the demand for transportation must be made. This involves determining the magnitude and character of both commodity flows and passenger movements. Traffic variation over time, average shipment size, and the nature of the cargo involved are of primary concern in describing the characteristics of the commodity movements. The nature and magnitude of these anticipated commodity flows will be the major determinants of the transport plan, although some basic network of transportation facilities will be dictated by the need to perform the minimum administrative, social, and military functions required of any responsible government. Second, the supply side of transportation must be investigated. Cost characteristics and differences in the quality of service for alternative modes of transportation and for alternative methods of production are of major concern here. There is, of course, considerable interaction between transport costs and the level of transport demand that eventually materializes. The final step involves evaluating/alternative transport solutions, taking into account the availability of factor inputs needed for the supply of transportation, differences in service quality, and differences in the indirect consequences associated with each alternative, as well as interactions between supply and demand.

Transportation demand derives both from the need to link together various centers of population and production within the region and from the need to link the region with the rest of the country and world markets. A basic network of regional transport routes, largely independent of the volumes of traffic that may materialize on the links of this network, is desirable for administrative, social, health, and security reasons. The purpose of such a network is largely communicative, and it is often characterized by considerations other than those that are purely economic.

Once the basic links connecting the region to the rest of the country have been provided, however, the nature of future additions to the transportation system depend more on the residual levels of traffic volume that materialize and cannot adequately be accommodated by the basic network. Here, the economic considerations associated with each new link in the system may become more important than the social considerations. This distinction between these two transportation networks is, of course, not always so clear, for in many cases basic routes can also be justified on economic grounds. In other cases, there are basic differences in the characteristics of the two transportation networks. The basic network, for example, is largely communicative in its purpose. In designing it, therefore, broad coverage, flexibility, and low initial cost are the necessary characteristics. With respect to these, a road system usually has no equivalent although there will be cases where a well-developed system of canal transportation may serve equally as well.

For the residual network, however, traffic flows are usually concentrated along a few major routes. By definition, traffic volumes are higher than can be handled by the basic network. Thus, operating and maintenance costs become relatively more important than initial costs, particularly to the extent that these affect the competitive position of the region for the production of various goods and services. Depending upon traffic volumes and the nature of the cargo, transport modes with cost characteristics different from highways may be of interest.

Predicting the demand for transportation in underdeveloped regions characteristically is complicated by the fact that past data upon which to base future predictions of transportation demand are usually lacking, either because the transport link under consideration is a completely new one for which no history exists, or simply because no attempts have been made to collect data in the past. Moreover, future developments are clouded with a great deal more uncertainty than usually exists in more advanced economies. A new road into an area where none previously existed may generate traffic beyond the wildest expectations of the planner, or it may generate a one-way, one-time flow of traffic out of the area into the existing centers of population. In other words, induced traffic (new traffic generated by the facility) is generally more significant in developing regions, and the element of uncertainty is always greater for induced traffic than for diverted traffic (existing traffic transferred from an old facility to the new one). Uncertainty also exists because many of the underdeveloped countries have specialized or "one-crop" economies with the result that small changes in the world markets for these goods can produce far-reaching effects on the total economy of the country.

Prediction of transport demand is further complicated by the fact that, as a derived demand, the demand for transportation depends upon the final demand for those commodities to be transported. The relevant demand functions for these commodities are usually unavailable in most situations. The major difficulty lies in determining the appropriate demand functions for products formerly not produced in the country. Often the demand characteristics of such presently nonexistent industries must be assumed on the basis of experience elsewhere. These characteristics may well differ under local conditions of production and distribution, or technology may have changed significantly by the time such activities become a reality. Moreover, the regional development plan is usually part of an over-all program to improve the per capita income throughout the country. Thus, even if sufficient data were available to determine present demand functions, the changing pattern of consumer tastes as incomes increase and as urbanization increases would be difficult to take into account.

On the supply side, the transportation planner is again faced with serious data problems. Some of these relate to the performance of existing transportation plant, such as facility life and maintenance requirements. Without a long history of transport development, for example, estimates of the economic life of various transport facilities are difficult to obtain unless such data are available for other countries having similar climatological and topographic characteristics. Facility life is an important factor in a capital-scarce economy, particularly where comparisons are being made between investment alternatives of different durability.

The most important supply problems, however, derive from the paucity of information on construction, operation, and maintenance costs of alternative modes of transportation and of alternative technologies within these modes. The availability of such data is in some ways more important than in well-developed countries where, as previously discussed, quasi-economic consequences often outweigh the strictly economic ones. Some inferences about the relevant cost data can be made, of course, by reference to cost experience in the more fully developed countries. These costs, however, are usually representative of types of transportation systems and methods of operation that are considered to be best engineering practice for the country involved. In developing regions, other methods may be preferred on grounds of economic efficiency.

In the case of roads, for example, underdeveloped regions are usually characterized by poor enforcement of traffic laws. One of the most notable violations is the overloading of trucks —a factor that must usually be taken into account when establishing the design standards to which roads are constructed. In addition, roads must often be built to higher standards than anticipated traffic volumes justify because of the uncertainty that normal maintenance practices will be carried out in the future. The political worth of a newly constructed highway generally outweighs the value of a well-maintained one. Where highway agencies have limited funds, therefore, pressures are for new construction as opposed to maintenance of existing plant. Moreover, because funds are usually allocated to highway agencies on a year-to-year basis by legislative bodies,[2] there is often considerable uncertainty that funds will be avail-

[2] Allocations must be made from general funds since user tax revenues are usually far below annual highway expenditures.

able for periodic maintenance when required. Without adequate maintenance (particularly in tropical climates), new roads deteriorate rapidly unless constructed to high standards. Poor law enforcement and uncertainty as to adequate maintenance practices thus tend to favor the overdesign of roads in underdeveloped regions.[3]

Other factors, such as a preponderance of mixed traffic, may influence the design of transport facilities in developing regions. Wagons with narrow, steel-rimmed wheels, for example, are particularly damaging to pavements. Such vehicles, together with inadequately illuminated bicycles and poorly marked obstructions, frequently make night driving in rural areas extremely hazardous. As a result, more traffic is shifted to daylight hours, thereby increasing the peaking characteristics of daily traffic patterns.

In view of these differences in the nature of transport problems, some differences in methods of planning transportation for developed and underdeveloped regions can reasonably be expected. Clearly, a strong case can be made for basing transportation policy in developing countries on firmer grounds than are customarily used in the more developed economies. The opportunity cost of ill-advised investments in transportation in terms of housing, educational, and medical investments forgone is a luxury which most developing countries can hardly afford.

Transportation facilities will nevertheless often be provided for political, social, administrative, or other reasons irrespective of the anticipated level of traffic demand for these facilities. Certain projects will be justified because they "strengthen national bonds by linking isolated regions to the rest of the country."[4] In such cases, the best transport alternative will be the one that minimizes the real cost of transportation and at

[3] The following statement made by a World Bank Mission to Venezuela supports this argument: "In short, we strongly urge that maintenance be built into highways by more adequate design." International Bank for Reconstruction and Development, *The Economic Development of Venezuela*, (Baltimore: The Johns Hopkins Press, 1961), p. 257.

[4] Gary Fromm, "Design of the Transport Sector," *Transport Investment and Economic Development*, Gary Fromm, ed. (Washington: The Brookings Institution, 1965), p. 93.

the same time places no undue restraints on the indirect benefits to be derived from the transportation investment.

One controversial aspect of the supply of transportation concerns techniques of production in the transportation industries. This is sometimes referred to as the "factor proportion problem." Much has been speculated about the relative desirability of labor- and capital-intensive methods of production in providing transportation for developing regions. Little, however, has been collected in the way of empirical data showing just what alternatives for production do exist. Whether or not a transportation system with a modern, expensive, fixed plant and low operating costs should be constructed depends upon the specific circumstances encountered: the available technical skills, the degree of certainty that future traffic estimates will materialize, the availability of capital inputs, and the priorities that must be forgone. Methods of taking these factors into account in evaluating alternative transportation investments is the main focus of the present work.

Particular emphasis is placed on the question of technological choice or substitutability of inputs, not just as between modes, but, more important, as between alternative technologies of a given mode. Road transport presents a particularly fertile and important field for the latter. Primary concern is with road transportation because in most developing countries investment in roads constitutes the most significant portion of total investment in the transport sector.

In Chapter Two, a framework for analyzing the degree of factor substitutability is developed. Empirical cost data illustrating the application of this framework for the case of road transportation in Venezuela are presented in Chapter Three. Chapter Four presents a case study of transportation planning in the newly developing area of Venezuela known as the Guayana region. In this example some intermodal comparisons are also made. Although this sort of analysis can best be carried out within the context of a specific set of conditions, such as those encountered in the Guayana region of Venezuela, the intention is to make the arguments as general as possible.

TECHNOLOGICAL CHOICE IN
THE SUPPLY OF TRANSPORTATION

Introduction

The cost of transporting goods from one point to another depends upon the manner in which these goods are moved. The manner most efficient in one country may not be the most efficient in another—an economic fact of life stemming from differences in the geography and productive factors with which each country finds itself endowed.

Selecting the best manner of providing transportation (or, for that matter, producing any good or service in the economy) is a problem in the choice of techniques of production. Certain goods, for example, can be produced using a variety of production techniques. The most efficient technique depends upon several factors, including the relative availability of different factors of production.

Interest in the problem of technological choice derives from the fact that most underdeveloped economies have factor endowments that differ from those of more developed economies, notably with respect to the relative scarcity of capital and skilled labor and the relative abundance of unskilled labor. Combinations of these factors of production other than those presently used in more developed economies may therefore be of interest. In particular, the capital requirements of alternative methods of providing transportation are of interest because the availability of capital is one of the major constraints on the rate of economic growth that can be achieved.

Due to the scarcity of capital in most underdeveloped

9

countries, heavy reliance is often placed on foreign loans or grants to help provide the capital investment necessary to achieve the desired rate of growth. Because the availability of such foreign capital is also limited, it is often useful to examine alternative investment proposals in terms of their foreign capital components as well as their total capital requirements.

Arguments have been made by development economists both for and against the use of capital-saving techniques of production in underdeveloped regions.[1] The use of labor-intensive technologies, for example, increases employment in what are characteristically high unemployment economies, thereby tending to reduce inequalities in the distribution of income. In addition, the expanded consumer market resulting from the increased purchasing power of labor may lead to economies of scale in the production of certain consumer goods. On the other hand, the use of labor-intensive techniques will characteristically be accompanied by a reduction in the rate of saving and the accumulation of capital available for reinvestment. In later stages of development, moreover, these labor-intensive techniques may lead to serious problems when it becomes desirable to shift to capital-intensive techniques and throw off job-making precedents. Experience with capital-intensive techniques of production during early stages of development may also be essential if the productivity of labor is to be improved.

In any event, selecting the proper technique of production depends upon knowing the range of technological choice which is available. Even where decisions are based on considerations other than economic efficiency, it is often of interest to know

[1] Some of the relevant literature includes: A. K. Sen, *Choice of Techniques, An Aspect of the Theory of Planned Economic Development* (Oxford: Basil Blackwell, 1960); R. S. Eckaus, "Technological Change in the Less Developed Areas" in *Development of the Emerging Countries, An Agenda for Research* (Washington: The Brookings Institution, 1962); Thirukodikoval N. Srinivasan, "Investment Criteria and Choice of Techniques of Production," *Yale Economic Essays II*, 1 (1962), (also Cowles Foundation Paper No. 177); and Walter Galenson and Harvey Leibenstein, "Investment Criteria, Productivity, and Economic Development," *Quarterly Journal of Economics, LXIX* (August, 1958).

which techniques of production are preferable from the economic point of view.

Consideration of the technological choice problem is particularly relevant in planning transportation because of the wide range of techniques that are possible in providing transportation facilities. An analysis of alternatives for capital substitution in transportation is also important because of the magnitude of investments in transportation in most developing countries. The foreign component of these investments is often considerable. Of development loans made by the World Bank between 1946 and 1963, for example, transportation accounted for 48, 43, and 32 per cent of total loans to Africa, Asia, and the Western Hemisphere, respectively.[2]

Finally, a knowledge of the capital requirements of various transportation modes is important in formulating economic models for regional planning. Considerable importance has been attached to the role of transport costs in determining the optimal spatial distribution of economic activities.[3] More recently, economic models have been developed that attempt to measure the interaction of transport investment and regional growth, and in particular to note the effect of changes in transport technology on over-all economic growth.[4]

The Range of Technology

It has been suggested that in designing transportation facilities for underdeveloped regions it is important to look at the whole range of technology that is available for meeting transport demand. By technology we mean a specific combination of productive factors, such as labor, capital, energy, or any other resource that can only be obtained at a certain cost.

[2] Wilfred Owen, *Strategy for Mobility* (Washington: The Brookings Institution, 1964), p. 154.

[3] See, for example, Louis Lefeber, *Allocation in Space, Production, Transport and Industrial Location* (Amsterdam: North Holland Publishing Co., 1958), p. 111.

[4] For an excellent description of one such model see Brian V. Martin and Charles B. Warden, "Transportation Planning in Developing Countries," *Traffic Quarterly, XXIX,* (January, 1965), pp. 59–75.

11

With different technologies it may be possible to produce similar results but at different costs. Thus goods may be moved over a given distance by human porters, by pack mules, by trucks, or by railroad boxcars. In each case, the technology is different, going from a very labor-intensive to a very capital-intensive method. These changes in technology are very distinct —mules for men, trucks for mules, or locomotives for trucks— and it is often a very simple matter to determine which technology is the most suitable. Where changes in technology are so distinct, where the medium by which the goods are carried changes, we define a change in transport *mode*.

Within a particular transport mode, further technological substitutions are also possible. Goods may be carried in many small trucks or fewer large trucks. The mode is the same although in each case the choice of technology is different. Similarly, goods may be carried by railroads around a mountain or through it, each case involving a different combination of construction and energy costs. For each mode there will be some technology or some combination of productive inputs that is best in terms of its use of available resources. When intermodal comparisons are made, as between road and rail, each mode should be compared using this best technology. It is important, therefore, to take a thorough look at the whole question of the substitutability of inputs, both as between modes and as between alternative combinations of factor inputs for a given mode. Some insight into the general nature of this substitutability in transport can be gained by considering a simple model that describes the production of transportation.

Transportation involves the transfer of weight between non-coincident points. This weight has a certain bulk and it can be moved between these two points along a path that may be circuitous or direct, easy or difficult, safe or hazardous. Moreover, it may move over this path swiftly or slowly, in units that are large or small. All these factors affect the cost of moving this weight to a greater or lesser extent.

A model that describes the production of transportation should at least take into account the more important of these factors. To some extent, the model should be sensitive to differences in (*a*) cargo characteristics (weight, bulk, density, and perishability), (*b*) route characteristics (circuity and difficulty), and (*c*) quality of transport (speed, safety, and reliability).

In the production of road transportation, for example, the major variables in the productive process include road alignment, road surface, vehicle size, and energy input. Alignment, road surface, and vehicle size usually constitute the independent variables, whereas energy input is usually a dependent variable. Our concern here is first to determine the possible combinations of these variables for a given level of transport production; second, to evaluate the costs associated with each combination; and third, to determine that combination of inputs which is best under the prevailing conditions of transport demand and factor costs. How these variables come into play to affect the cost of transport and to what extent they may be substituted for one another can be described in the following manner.

Consider the problem of designing a road to carry a particular axle load. The load-carrying capacity or strength of a road depends primarily on the strength of the subgrade (material over which the road is to be constructed) and the thickness of the pavement structure that is placed on the subgrade. The relationship between these three factors can be shown (Figure 2.1) by a three-dimensional surface in which the vertical axis represents pavement thickness and the horizontal axes represent subgrade strength and allowable axle load. By cutting this surface with a series of vertical sections, strength contours can be obtained, each of which indicates the various combinations of pavement thickness and subgrade strength that will safely support the given load. These strength contours (Figure 2.2) can be derived by theory, and their shape is independent of local conditions.

Local conditions become important in determining the costs of providing the pavement structure and of preparing the subgrade material. Subgrade strength, for example, can be improved by compaction or soil-stabilization methods. The cost of improving the subgrade, however, will depend upon local

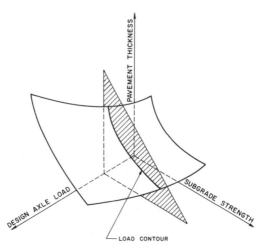

FIGURE 2.1. *The relationship among axle load, subgrade strength, and pavement thickness.*

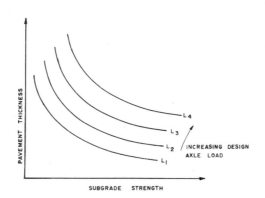

FIGURE 2.2. *Road strength isoquants.*

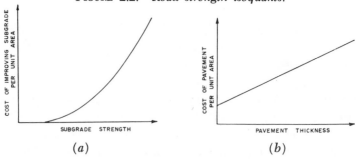

FIGURE 2.3. *Subgrade strength and pavement thickness cost functions.*

conditions, such as the nature of the soil, the availability and cost of labor, and the cost of equipment. As the subgrade is improved, total costs might vary in the general way shown in Figure 2.3. Similarly, the cost of increasing pavement thickness will also depend upon local conditions.

The cost relationships of Figure 2.3 can be combined to form a series of equal cost contours or "isocost" curves as shown in Figure 2.4. Each isocost curve indicates the various

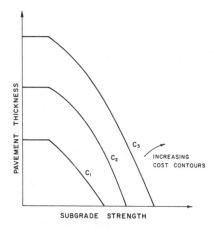

FIGURE 2.4. *Road strength isoquants.*

ways in which a stated expenditure can be divided between improving the subgrade and providing additional pavement. At one extreme, the total amount can be spent on subgrade improvements leaving nothing for pavement expenditure, while at the other extreme, the total amount may be spent on pavement. In each case, the intercepts are obtained from Figure 2.3 by observing what subgrade strength and pavement thickness, respectively, can be obtained for the given expenditure. In the intermediate range, the available amount of money is divided in varying proportions between the two alternative methods of increasing road strength. If the isocost map is now superimposed on the strength contour map (Figure 2.2), the minimum cost of providing a specified road strength will be given by the isocost curve that is just tangent to the corresponding strength contour. This is shown in Figure 2.5. Moving in either direction from this point of tangency along the strength contour involves moving to a higher isocost curve.

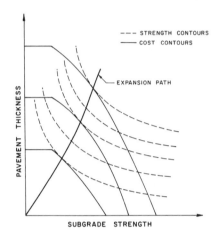

FIGURE 2.5. *Road strength expansion path.*

For example, if a road is to be designed to carry some load *L*, and if we start with a design in which no pavement layer is included, expenditures for pavement thickness can be substituted advantageously for investments in improving the subgrade up to some point beyond which it will no longer be advantageous to continue the substitution. This point depends upon the relative cost functions for improving the subgrade and providing additional pavement (Figure 2.3). If these relative cost functions change, the shape of the isocost curves will change and some new point of tangency will be indicated corresponding to a different combination of subgrade strength and pavement thickness. In other words, the proper design or choice of technology *clearly depends upon the relative factor costs.*

Each point of tangency indicates a particular value of road strength and the minimum cost of providing this strength. The locus of all such points, or "expansion path," can be replotted as in Figure 2.6 to show the variation of minimum total road construction costs with increases in load carrying capacity. As factor prices change, the shape of this cost curve will also change.

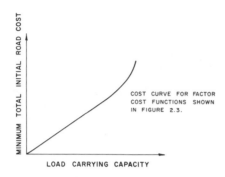

FIGURE 2.6. *Minimum total road cost function.*

A similar technique can also be used to illustrate the substitution effects possible between road conditions and vehicle operating costs. For a vehicle of a given size, road conditions (alignment and surface) determine vehicle performance (speed) as well as the energy required to move the vehicle over a given distance. For purposes of illustration the major characteristic of road conditions is considered to be the average rate of rise and fall; fuel consumption is taken as a measure of vehicle performance. Using these parameters, volume contours or isoquant curves can be drawn (Figure 2.7) that

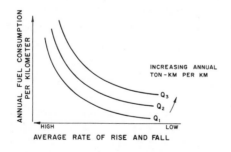

FIGURE 2.7. *Transport output isoquants.*

17

indicate the quantity of goods that can be moved over a given distance for various combinations of fuel inputs and road conditions. If, for example, road conditions are improved by reducing the average rate of rise and fall, the quantity of fuel necessary to carry a specified tonnage will decrease correspondingly. Changing the vehicle size may change the shape of the isoquants if there is a significant change in the ratio of vehicle tare weight to payload.

Other factors, notably horizontal curvature, sight distances, and road surface, affect road conditions by contributing to the resistance encountered by a vehicle moving over the road. A high-resistance alignment, for example, might consist of a rough surface fitted to existing terrain with only minor quantities of earth removed. A low-resistance alignment, on the other hand, might consist of a smooth (concrete or asphalt) level pavement involving considerable earthwork quantities. Similarly, operating costs include components other than fuel consumption, of which the most important are travel time, tire wear, and vehicle maintenance. In addition, road maintenance costs associated with different levels of transportation output must also be taken into account. However, since the purpose here is to indicate only the nature of the substitutability possible between road improvements and vehicle operating costs, consideration of fuel consumption and rate of rise and fall is sufficient for purposes of illustration.[5]

The cost of reducing the average rate of rise and fall of a particular road depends primarily on local topography and geology. To a lesser extent the availability of labor and heavy earth-moving equipment also influences this cost. With increasing expenditures, road conditions can be improved up to some point beyond which further expenditures will yield only slight improvements. Thus, for practical purposes, the cost curve can be considered as asymptotic to the lowest rates of rise and fall

[5] For a more detailed discussion of the relationship between road conditions and vehicle operating costs, see A. S. Lang and D. H. Robbins, "A New Technique for Predicting Vehicle Operating Cost," *Operational Effects of Design and Traffic Engineering*, Bulletin 308 (Washington: Highway Research Board, 1962), pp. 19–35.

possible. As shown in Figure 2.8, the more rugged the terrain, the higher the cost of reaching this point. Figure 2.9 shows the cost curve for fuel consumption, assumed to be linear.

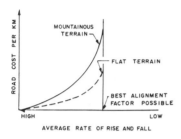

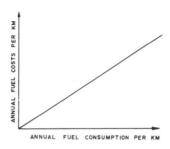

FIGURE 2.8. *Alignment factor cost function.*

FIGURE 2.9. *Operating factor cost function.*

In Figure 2.4 the units of each axis represent initial or capital costs, thus allowing the costs to be combined in an isocost map. In the case of Figures 2.8 and 2.9, however, the fuel costs are variable costs that continue over the life of the facility, and the road cost is a fixed or one-time cost incurred in constructing the facility. To be comparable, therefore, these fuel or current inputs must be aggregated in some manner, or, alternatively, fixed inputs must be expressed on an annual basis. In aggregating current inputs, for example, future inputs must be discounted by a factor that depends upon the appropriate rate of interest and upon the time period during which the input is required. Methods of aggregating these inputs are treated in more detail in a later section of this chapter (p. 28 ff).

If the costs of Figure 2.8 are amortized on an annual basis, an isocost map now can be plotted and superimposed on the isoquant diagram (Figure 2.10). Again the tangency points indicate the degree to which operating inputs can advantageously be substituted for road improvements. At each point of tangency, both a total cost and a volume of transport output are indicated so that the expansion path through these points

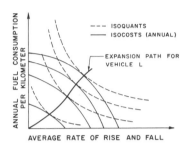

FIGURE 2.10. *Transport output expansion path.*

represents the minimum total cost curve for the given vehicle
L when only road construction costs and fuel costs are considered.

In these considerations of alignment and operating factors
vehicle size has been considered as given. If the vehicle size
is changed, a new point of tangency will be determined resulting from the changed shape of the isoquants (Figure 2.7).
Thus for each vehicle size a different cost curve will be
obtained. When these curves are plotted together, as in Figure
2.11, the optimum vehicle size is given as a function of transport output.

In the generalized case, however, vehicle size or load-carrying capacity of the roads can be taken into account by adding
a third dimension to Figure 2.7. The isoquant curves would
become surfaces of equal transport output and Figure 2.7

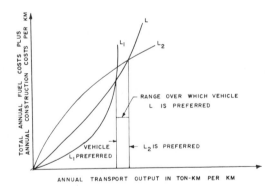

FIGURE 2.11. *Minimum total transport output cost function.*

would represent a section through these surfaces taken perpendicular to the vehicle size axis. In other words, a particular surface would indicate the various combinations of energy input, vehicle size, and road conditions that would result in the production of the same output of transportation. This surface would be entirely independent of local conditions and would represent a relationship between physical inputs (or productive factors) and the quantity of transportation produced. The slope of the surface measured parallel to any axis would indicate the rate at which one factor could be substituted for another without changing the level of transport output.

In a similar fashion, isocost surfaces can be found that are functions of the same physical parameters. These surfaces, however, would be entirely dependent upon local conditions—they represent particular solutions. Again, as in the two-dimensional case, points of tangency would indicate optimal points of production, optimal in the sense that output is maximized for a given cost, or that cost is minimized for a given output. The expansion path through these points would specify, in addition to the best combination of road conditions and operating cost, the best vehicle size to be used.

Several qualifications, of course, should be made with regard to the validity of this model. In the first place, many of the relationships between factors probably do not exist as they have been described. The model, for example, assumes continuous surfaces or perfect substitutability of inputs, where in fact indivisibilities or discontinuities are bound to exist. This would be particularly true in the case of railroads, where the minimum design standards for the supporting medium are probably more rigid than for highways.

Second, the heterogeneity and number of the factors to be considered make the use of two-dimensional diagrams impractical in real situations. In the preceding discussion, transportation output was related to the physical quantities of the necessary inputs utilized. This relationship between output and physical inputs is often referred to as a production function. Most of the input factors that go into the production of transportation, however, cannot be readily expressed in homogeneous units; it is difficult to define a physical operating input that accounts for fuel consumed, vehicle wear and tear, vehicle depreciation, and drivers' time and that at the same time is very meaningful or practical. The isoquant relationships described would then have to be replaced by equations containing these various factors. In addition, there is the problem of determining a very meaningful measure of transportation output itself.[6]

Third, many factors have been omitted so as to facilitate description of the substitution relationships. As a practical matter, for example, trip length must be included since vehicle use, as well as various unit overhead costs, will be seriously influenced by this variable. Terminal costs and road maintenance costs must also be taken into account. Terminal costs represent one area where considerable substitutability of labor for capital equipment is possible. Although maintenance costs are difficult to determine because their variability with changes in traffic is not well understood, they can be accounted for within the framework described.

Finally, variations in traffic volume or levels of transport production over time have not been taken into account. In developing areas, investments in transportation facilities may be followed by a rapid growth in traffic, particularly where transport routes were previously nonexistent. The question then arises as to what level of traffic the transport facility should be designed to accommodate.

Despite some of these problems, which are treated at greater length later in this chapter, the model described here serves as a useful conceptual tool for analyzing the degree of factor substitutability possible in the production of road transportation. Many of the relationships that have been described, moreover, are applicable to analyzing factor substitutability within other modes of transportation.

[6] Nothing has been said about the problem of measuring transportation output. A weight × distance measure has been assumed here for illustrative purposes. Some of the problems of measuring transport output are excellently summarized in George W. Wilson, "On the Output Unit in Transportation," *Land Economics*, XXXV, 3 (August, 1959), pp. 266–76.

The Nature of Substitutability in Road Transportation

Despite certain oversimplifications, the model described gives some indication of the nature of the substitutability that is possible between factor inputs in producing road transportation. It shows, for example, how improvements to the subgrade can be substituted for increases in pavement thickness to provide a road of a specified strength. Substitution possibilities within this example could be carried even further. In compacting the subgrade, alternative types of equipment, such as large, heavy-duty compaction equipment requiring only a few passes over the subgrade, or lighter equipment requiring many passes, might be used. In the first case, the capital component per unit area compacted will probably be greater, whereas in the second case the labor component is likely to be more important. Thus just as load contours (Figure 2.2) were drawn showing the substitutability of pavement thickness for subgrade strength, subgrade strength contours could be obtained showing the substitutability of labor for capital.

In a similar manner, pavement thickness contours could be drawn showing the substitutability of the same inputs for one another. High labor inputs might correspond to methods of construction employing hand mixers for asphalt or concrete, whereas high capital inputs might indicate the use of large automatic paving machines.

This type of substitutability is representative of the different levels of capital intensity possible in the construction of transportation facilities. For a given final design (specified in terms of road width, pavement thickness, etc.), it deals with the alternative methods of construction that can be used to arrive at this design. Within various stages of the construction process the range of possible alternatives will differ. A wide range of capital intensity exists, for example, between the use of head baskets, wheelbarrows, and bulldozers for earthwork excavation.[7]

[7] An extreme example of the use of labor-intensive techniques for earthwork is given by the construction of an irrigation canal in China, where 1.3 million workers moved 2.5 billion cubic feet of earth without the use of machinery.

In comparing the relative desirability of labor and capital-intensive methods of construction, several factors should be kept in mind. One concerns the destabilizing effect which large labor-intensive works might have following the completion of a project. Strong pressures would undoubtedly result to undertake more heavy construction projects in order to provide further employment for the work force released from the project. This pressure would exist in any event, but its magnitude would increase to some extent with increasing labor intensity.

In addition, labor-intensive methods of construction will generally require longer times for completion.[8] In part, the time saved on preliminary construction of access facilities for heavy equipment might compensate for any additional construction time where lighter equipment is to be used. Moreover, even where heavy equipment is used, the experience in many developing countries is that a great deal of time is lost because of inefficient handling and repair of equipment.[9]

The use of labor-intensive methods of construction may also affect the design of facilities to some extent. Labor-intensive techniques, for example, would favor the use of concrete over steel for the construction of highway structures, and could also influence the choice between asphalt and concrete highway surfaces. There may also be significant differences in the final quality of work between labor and capital-intensive methods of construction. Finally, a proper evaluation of labor-intensive methods of construction should take into account additional overhead costs, such as food and housing. These costs may be considerable on large labor-intensive projects carried out in remote areas.

Kanwar Sain and K. L. Rao, *Report on the Recent River Valley Projects in China* (New Delhi: Government of India, Central Water and Power Commission, 1955), as quoted in United Nations, "Capital Intensity in Heavy Engineering Construction," *Bulletin on Industrialization and Productivity*, No. 1 (April, 1958), p. 37.

[8] It is worth noting in this respect that the Chinese irrigation project cited previously took only 80 days to complete.

[9] See, for example, E. K. Hawkins, *Roads and Road Transport in an Underdeveloped Country, A Case Study of Uganda* (London: Her Majesty's Stationery Office, 1962), p. 199.

The degree to which labor can be effectively substituted for capital in the construction of transportation facilities is an important issue to be considered in planning transportation for underdeveloped countries.[10] Moreover, it is an issue that has equal importance in planning irrigation, electrification, or other civil engineering projects. Basically, however, it represents a problem in engineering construction, and as such is beyond the scope of this work.[11] In the following discussions, therefore, where costs of construction are used, they are assumed to represent those obtained from current methods of construction.

Once the decision to build a transportation facility using certain methods of construction has been made, a second type of substitutability is possible. This is the substitutability at fixed levels of investment among the labor, material, and capital inputs necessary to operate and maintain the facility.

Highway maintenance costs, for example, can be substituted for vehicle operating costs. By maintaining a road to a high standard, vehicle depreciation per unit of transportation can be reduced due to increased vehicle utilization. Furthermore, labor-capital substitutions are also possible within the maintenance operation itself.[12]

[10] Lest the reader think that such techniques are restricted to countries where unskilled labor is so cheap that earthwork can be carried out using head baskets, an example of the use of labor-intensive techniques in constructing an earth dam in Poland is of interest. Here labor was used not for the transport of the excavated earth itself but for building a narrow-gauge railroad track. This roundabout labor-intensive technique thus used labor to produce high-productivity capital equipment that was then used to transport the excavated earth. See United Nations, "Capital Intensity and Costs in Earth-Moving Operations," *Bulletin on Industrialization and Productivity,* No. 3 (March, 1960), p. 15.

[11] For further discussion of the choice of construction techniques in developing countries, the reader is referred to articles in the *Bulletin on Industrialization and Productivity,* published by the United Nations Department of Economic and Social Affairs, particularly Nos. 1 (April 1958) and 3 (March, 1960).

[12] For a good discussion of this, see Hawkins, *op. cit.,* pp. 197–199. It should be noted, however, that one of the major difficulties involved in any consideration of highway maintenance costs concerns differentiation between pure maintenance and maintenance that actually upgrades the road to a higher standard than the original construction, thereby representing a capital improvement.

Probably the most important substitutions within the operating phase (certainly for any reasonable degree of traffic) relate primarily to vehicle size and utilization. Vehicle size, for example, determines the quantity of fuel, the hours of driver time, and the proportion of total vehicle maintenance and depreciation that must be charged against each ton-kilometer produced. For certain types of vehicles, the quantities of each of these input factors per unit weight moved will be higher than for other vehicles, and it would be clearly inefficient to use such types of vehicles. It is for vehicles where more of one factor and less of others is required that the nature of the substitutability becomes interesting.

Finally, a third type of substitutability can be considered that represents a combination of the two types just described. This concerns the substitutability of current or variable inputs for fixed inputs. Current inputs depend upon traffic demand. They include those factors used in operating vehicles and in maintaining the road. Fixed inputs, on the other hand, are those used in providing the road in the first place.[13] For each type of road, corresponding to a particular fixed investment, alternative combinations of variable inputs can be used in producing a specified output of transportation. At one extreme, light, single-unit vehicles might be used over poorly graded, unpaved roads, while at the other extreme, heavy, multiple-unit vehicles traveling on superhighways might be employed. The problem that is of greatest interest concerns the substitutability within all possible combinations of the construction and operating phases.

The number of such combinations of capital and current cost combinations can, of course, be extremely large. For each level of traffic, for example, seventy-five alternatives could be considered, allowing for only five different road types, three surface types, and five vehicle sizes. In the final analysis, the judgment and experience of the engineer will determine which set of alternatives seems most feasible. Improved methods of analysis and computation, however, are rapidly making it

[13] Strictly speaking, these are short-run fixed inputs since in the long run almost all costs can be considered to be variable.

possible for the engineer to consider a much wider range of alternatives than has previously been the case.[14]

For each level of fixed investment some combination of operating inputs will be optimal when the level of traffic volume to be accommodated is taken into account. This can be shown graphically, as in Figure 2.12, and explained in the following manner.

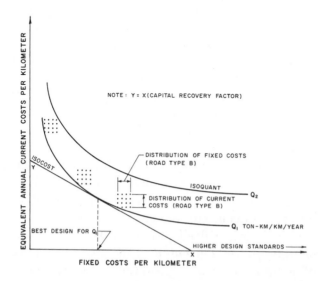

FIGURE 2.12. *Substitutability between current and fixed inputs.*

As discussed previously, several methods of construction can be used to provide a road of a given standard or design. Each method will involve different labor, local currency, and foreign exchange components, leading to a distribution of fixed costs when each of these components is valued at its true cost. This

[14] See, for example, Paul O. Roberts and A. Villaveces, *DTM* (*Digital Terrain Model*) *Design System* (Cambridge, Mass.: Civil Engineering Systems Laboratory, Massachusetts Institute of Technology, 1961), Research Report R62-6. A program has also been developed in conjunction with this to compute the vehicle operating costs associated with a particular trial design. See A. S. Lang, P. O. Roberts, and D. H. Robbins, "An Evaluation of Techniques for Highway User Cost Computation," *Studies in Highway Engineering Economy*, Bulletin 320 (Washington: Highway Research Board, 1962), pp. 1–11.

distribution is represented in Figure 2.12 by rows of dots for several hypothetical road types. Similarly, holding the traffic volume constant, for each point in the distribution of fixed costs it is possible to set a distribution of current costs that corresponds to various combinations of labor and working capital (local currency and foreign exchange). This distribution is shown by the columns of dots. Thus, for each type of road, alternative combinations of fixed and current costs (at constant levels of traffic) are shown by a rectangular array of points on the graph. Each point in the array corresponds to a certain combination of labor and capital used in constructing the facility initially, and in operating it thereafter. If these factors have been valued at their real costs, the curve passing through the lower left-hand corner of each array defines the substitutability of labor for capital for all lowest cost combinations of fixed and operating inputs.[15]

Before the isoquants of Figure 2.12 can be made completely operational, two problems must now be considered. The first concerns the method of aggregating future current expenditures. The second deals with the prices to be used in evaluating the real costs of various fixed and operating factor inputs.

Discounting future current expenditures. The purpose of discounting future current expenditures is to reduce them to their proper scale and provide them with the same dimensions as initial fixed costs. In order to compare initial fixed costs of construction with annual current expenditures, one of two methods is usually employed. The first is widely used by economists. It involves reducing the future stream of current costs to their present discounted value. The present discounted value of a current expenditure in some future year j is given by the term $uV_j/(1+i)^j$, where

u = average current expenditure per unit of transport output

V_j = transport output in year j

i = rate of interest.

[15] The curves of Figure 2.12 represent the labor-capital substitutions possible in providing road transportation. Were similar analyses to be carried

The present discounted value of all future expenditures is determined by summing these terms for each year in the period under consideration.

Engineers, on the other hand, often use a method in which initial fixed costs of construction are amortized on an annual basis. The amortization factor, known as the Capital Recovery Factor, is defined as a factor that, when multiplied by the *present* investment (or future costs which have already been discounted), gives the uniform end-of-year payment necessary to repay the debt in n years. Numerically,[16] it is equal to $i(1+i)^n/[(1+i)^n - 1]$ where

$$i = \text{rate of interest}$$
$$n = \text{life of the facility in years.}$$

Using this method, the annual costs of amortizing the fixed costs of construction are compared with annual current costs for some equivalent annual traffic. The equivalent annual traffic volume similarly is determined by expressing the present discounted value of future volumes on an annual basis.[17] Thus

---

out for other modes of transport, substitution relationships could be obtained showing the possible combinations of factor inputs over a much wider range of fixed and current costs.

[16] Derivation of the Capital Recovery Factor is shown in Eugene L. Grant and W. Grant Ireson, *Principles of Engineering Economy* (New York: The Ronald Press Company, 1960), Chapter 4. In other terms, the Capital Recovery Factor is identical to the Sinking Fund Factor plus the interest rate.

[17] Grant and Ireson, *op. cit.*, p. 90 state

Where disbursements are expected to vary . . . from year to year . . . it is necessary first to convert all disbursements to present worth before converting to equivalent uniform annual cost.

Economists may be somewhat confused by this procedure. If one takes the trouble to determine the present worth of a future stream of annual costs, then the entire analysis might as well be carried out on the basis of present values. For a variety of reasons, however, engineers often prefer to "annualize" all costs (as in the case of applying the Capital Recovery Factor to initial construction costs). In such cases the appropriate volume for which to compute annual costs is given by Equation 2.1a. Where annual traffic volumes are anticipated to increase uniformly, for example, use of the arithmetic average of future volumes would overstate annual costs for any interest rate other than zero.

$$u \, \text{EAV} = \text{CRF} \sum_{j=1}^{n} \frac{uV_j}{(1+i)^j} \qquad (2.1)$$

and

$$\text{EAV} = \text{CRF} \sum_{j=1}^{n} \frac{V_j}{(1+i)^j} \qquad (2.1a)$$

where

EAV = equivalent annual volume

n = number of years in the time period under consideration

CRF = capital recovery factor.

The formula for equivalent annual volume can be simplified when the increases in volume are expected to vary arithmetically or geometrically. If the annual *numerical* increment in traffic is expected to remain constant then[18]

$$\text{EAV} = V_1 + \frac{b}{i} - \frac{nb}{i} \, (\text{CRF} - i) \qquad (2.2)$$

where

V_1 = annual traffic volume in the first year

b = annual numerical increment in volume.

If the annual *percentage* increment in traffic is expected to remain constant at k, then[19]

$$\text{EAV} = \text{CRF} \left[\frac{V_1}{(1+i)^{n-1}} \quad \frac{(1+i)^n - (1+k)^n}{i-k} \right] \qquad (2.3)$$

In either case, values of equivalent annual volume can be tabulated or shown graphically for various values of b, k, i, and

[18] The formula is shown without derivation in Clarkson H. Oglesby and Laurence I. Hewes, *Highway Engineering*, Second Edition (New York: John Wiley & Sons, Inc., 1964), p. 85. Alternatively, gradient factors to convert a gradient series to an equivalent uniform annual series can be used. See Grant and Ireson, *op. cit.*, Table E-23, p. 560.

[19] Adapted from an equation for the present value of a stream of net benefits shown in Hawkins, *op. cit.*, p. 176.

n. Depending on how unit current expenditures are defined, equivalent annual volume might be expressed in terms of vehicle-kilometers or 1000 ton-kilometers per year.

Valuation of factor inputs. In most underdeveloped countries a wide discrepancy may exist between the market prices of various factors of production and real costs of these factors to the economy. These real costs are sometimes referred to as social, shadow, or accounting prices. They are fictitious prices attached to some factor inputs in order to give a better approximation of their relative importance to the economy.[20]

The valuation of capital inputs is one important example of the discrepancy between market and accounting prices. Where capital is scarce, real interest rates are likely to be high. Often, however, interest rates may be set at some artificially lower rate for various social or political reasons. If this official rate is used in evaluating alternative methods of production, there will be a tendency to use methods that are more capital-intensive than might be used under strict adherence to rules of economic efficiency.[21]

Valuation of foreign exchange rates is another instance where the official prices tend to undervalue the real cost to the economy. The foreign component of transportation investments creates a gap in the balance of payments that must be met either by increasing exports or by reducing imports to other sectors of the economy. Often, however, additional export capacity does not exist, and competition for the available imports raises their true economic cost above that obtained by valuing these imports at the official rate of exchange. This effect on the balance of payments is often considered to be one of the most important factors in evaluating alternative transportation proj-

---

[20] United Nations Economic Commission for Asia and the Far East, *Programming Techniques For Economic Development* (Bangkok, 1960), p. 40.

[21] The problem of choosing the appropriate rate of interest can sometimes be circumvented by employing the rate of return method of evaluation. For a more detailed discussion see Hans A. Adler, "Economic Evaluation of Transport Projects" in *Transport Investment and Economic Development*, Gary Fromm, ed. (Washington: The Brookings Institution, 1965), pp. 192–194.

ects.[22] It seems logical in any event that payments made abroad should be separated out and weighted more heavily than equivalent payments made domestically.[23]

A significant discrepancy between market and accounting prices may also exist in the case of labor costs. The tendency here, however, is to overvalue the labor component. Real labor costs depend upon the loss of production in activities from which it may be withdrawn. If a road is to be constructed in an area where unemployment is high, wages paid to unskilled labor may be considerably higher than the real cost to the economy, since this labor would otherwise remain unemployed. Secondary effects such as the expenditure of these newly acquired wages on commodities that are already in short supply may tend to reduce the disparity between the wage rate and real costs. The wage rate paid to skilled labor may even understate its real cost. In general, however, the wage rate paid is usually higher than the opportunity cost of using labor and a shadow price is needed to evaluate properly the real cost of labor.

The net effect of these discrepancies between market and accounting prices, namely, the undervaluation of capital and foreign exchange components and the overestimation of labor costs, would be to allocate higher priority to capital-intensive projects. Therefore, in considering alternative techniques of producing transportation, labor, foreign exchange, and local currency components should be determined, and attempts made to evaluate them individually. Methods have been developed for making adjustments to market prices, which, al-

[22] The following quotation from a Chilean Transport Study illustrates the point:

The primary bottleneck to the economic development of Chile is the lack of foreign exchange. For this reason it is essential to have a separate study of the impact on the balance of payments of the different transport investment projects and of the operation of the different transport media.

Robert Tennant Brown, *Programming Investments in Transport, The Chilean Experience* (unpublished doctoral dissertation in Economics, deposited in Harvard College Library, 1961), p. 63.

[23] Moreover, it is often necessary to determine foreign components for other reasons. Loans made by the World Bank, for example, are limited to the foreign components of projects that it finances.

though by no means exact, should be used to investigate the effect of accounting prices on the selection among alternative projects.[24]

Selection of the Optimal Technology

Given the range of possible alternatives as described by Figure 2.12, the question then arises as to how to select that combination of factor inputs or choice of technology which is optimal. In practical terms this means selecting both the standards to be used in constructing a highway facility and the type of vehicle to be used. Figure 2.12 describes the substitutability of current for fixed expenditures. Since a particular level of fixed investment corresponds to a certain type of road and since current expenditures indicate a particular operating procedure, these curves also show the degree to which alternative technologies are substitutable for one another.

Isocost curves can again be used to select that technology or combination of current and fixed expenditures which is best. In this case, however, the isocost curves indicate the combinations of annual current expenditures over a period of years and the initial fixed investment that can be obtained for a specified sum of capital in the present. In other words, the isocost curve specifies the alternative ways of spending an available quantity of capital. On one hand, the entire sum may be invested in fixed expenditures, leaving nothing for future current expenditures. This case gives the X intercept of the isocost curve shown in Figure 2.12. On the other hand, the entire sum may be set aside to provide for an annual operating expenditure, denoted by the Y intercept, which is determined by the appropriate rate of interest and the assumed period of amortization. (Thus, the Y intercept equals the X intercept multiplied by the Capital Recovery Factor.) In the intermediate range a portion of the total sum is invested in capital expenditure, while the remainder is set aside to meet current expenditures. As before, the optimal point of production or choice of technology

[24] These are summarized in the United Nations, *Manual on Economic Development* (New York, 1958), p. 203 ff.

will be given where the isocost curves are tangent to the isoquants.

The expansion path obtained by connecting all such points of tangency will indicate the minimum total cost of providing road transportation as output varies. The shape of this cost curve will vary according to the rate of interest. If several alternative modes of transport or combinations of modes are analyzed in a manner similar to the one described here for road transport, their final cost curves can be compared, thus showing over what ranges of traffic volume and for what interest rates each mode or combination of modes is to be preferred. In other words, once minimum total cost curves for each mode have been determined in the manner suggested here, intermodal comparisons can be made.

The following example illustrates an application of this method of analysis. Based on data presented in Chapter Three, estimates of total annual current costs for a particular route in southeastern Venezuela were computed for each year of a ten-year period beginning in 1966. Construction costs were also estimated for each of several road types. When the current costs for each year were discounted and expressed as an equivalent annual volume, it was then possible to describe the substitutability between current and fixed expenditures as shown in Figure 2.13. In order to make the axes comparable, fixed costs were amortized on an annual basis at an interest rate of 10%. The substitution relationship is shown by Curve 1 and the best technology is determined by the point of tangency between this isoquant and the isocost corresponding to 59,000 bolivars.

Figure 2.13 also illustrates the effect of using accounting prices on the selection of final design standards. For each of the three isoquants shown, the optimum level of fixed investment (corresponding to a particular set of design standards) is different. Lowering the real wage rate, for example, improves the position of the higher current cost alternative since current expenditures (vehicle operation and road maintenance) have higher labor components than construction expenditures.

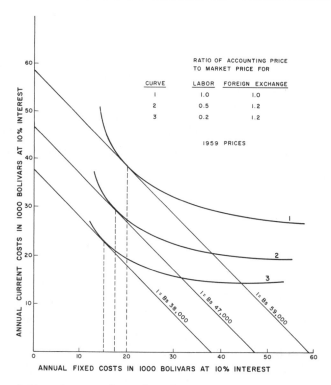

FIGURE 2.13. *An example of the selection of optimal road investment.*

TECHNOLOGICAL CHOICE AND THE COST OF ROAD TRANSPORTATION IN VENEZUELA

Introduction

In the preceding chapter, methods of analyzing factor substitutability and selecting the optimal combination of factor inputs for the production of a specific output of transportation have been treated. Most of the diagrams presented to back up the arguments are dimensionless, showing by argument alone the general shape of curves and the characteristics of the relationships involved. The purpose of the present chapter is to consider some of the practical applications of these relationships.

Probably the most serious objection to the method of approach described previously concerns the practicability of obtaining data that are both reliable and in the required form. It may be argued that in most developing regions the transport needs are so great—and in many cases, so obvious—that data collection of the nature suggested could hardly be justified, either with respect to the funds that would have to be allocated, or on grounds of the time necessary to complete such data collection operations. The merits of this argument really depend upon an analysis of the benefits to be reaped by such data collection and the costs of acquisition.

Four types of data are required if a thorough analysis of factor substitutability is to be made and if the best combination of factor inputs is to be determined. These data requirements can be illustrated by the use of a simple flow chart, as shown in Figure 3.1, giving the relationships between choice of technology, states of nature, and final costs of transportation.

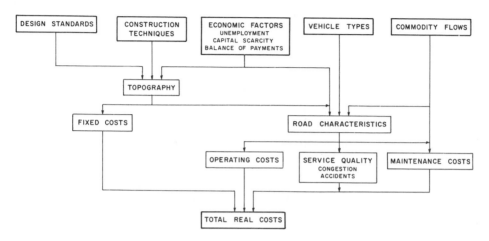

FIGURE 3.1. *The effect of choice of techniques on road transportation costs.*

In Figure 3.1, choice of technology is represented by (*a*) choice of standards to be used in designing the transport facility, (*b*) selection of the methods of construction, and (*c*) the selection of methods of using the facility in terms of the size and type of vehicle to be employed. Varying any one of these three basic "choice parameters" affects the final total cost of transportation by way of the linkages shown in the flow chart. Data requirements derive from the need to describe the relationships between the choice parameters (techniques of production) and end results (final real costs).

In order to describe the relationships of Figure 3.1 in quantitative terms, the required data are briefly those illustrating:

1. The effect of changes in construction techniques on the costs of constructing a road to give design standards.

2. The effect of changing design standards on total costs of construction (using in each case the best method as determined by 1) and on road maintenance costs in different kinds of terrain.

3. The effect of changing design standards in various types of terrain on the quality of the final road as described by such measures as average grade, curvature, and design speed.

4. The effect of changing vehicle size and type on the unit costs of carrying goods over roads constructed to various design standards in various types of terrain.

Of these, the first will not be considered further for reasons already discussed in the preceding chapter. Aside from variations in construction techniques, and given (a) terrain conditions and (b) final volume, the variations that are of major concern are those that relate to the choice of design standards and the selection of vehicle size. The former determines the fixed or initial cost of providing the transportation facility, whereas the latter affects the current costs associated with using the facility. Both affect the annual cost of maintaining the facility.

In Part I, the variation in fixed costs produced by changes in design standards is discussed in more detail. Current costs are considered in Part II. The variation in combined fixed and current costs is treated in Part III.

PART I. FIXED COSTS

Design Standards and Construction Costs

One of the most frequently asked and most difficult questions to answer pertaining to transportation facilities is "How much does it cost to build?" The difficulty of placing a cost on the construction of transportation facilities of any type results from the large number of factors that enter into any consideration of construction costs. In constructing roads to identical standards in different areas, for example, differences may be encountered in topography, nature of the soil, drainage conditions, the availability of materials for construction, and the accessibility to labor, supplies, and materials during construction. All these factors influence the final costs of constructing the road.

In addition to these variations in the states of nature encountered, variations in the standards used introduce further differences in construction costs. These differences cannot always be traced back to differences in particular standards, as changes in one geometric standard are often accompanied by changes in others. In all but very flat terrain, for example, changes in design speed will generally lead to differences in lane width, curvature, and sight distances, each of which will affect costs of construction. The various states of nature and design standards that influence road construction costs are summarized in Table 3.1. Because of the relative magnitude of the costs involved, pavement costs are discussed separately in the following section. Right-of-way or land acquisition costs are not considered as these are usually unimportant for the construction of rural roads in underdeveloped regions.

Design speed is the most important single standard affecting the construction costs of two-lane highways. Design speed de-

Table 3.1. A Summary of Factors Affecting Highway Construction Costs

Cost Elements	States of Nature	Design Standards
Preparation of Site	Topography	Design Speed Width Sight Distances
Earthwork	Terrain Soil Geology	Design Speed Width Sight Distances Maximum Gradient Maximum Curvature
Structures	Terrain Soil Geology	Width Design Axle Load Axle Spacing Design Volume
Drainage Structures	Terrain Soil Climate Geology	Width Design Axle Load Axle Spacing Design Volume
Pavement	Terrain Soil Geology Climate	Width Design Axle Load Axle Spacing Design Volume

termines the necessary safe-stopping and passing sight distances to be incorporated into the highway design. The latter, in turn, have a significant effect on the capacity of undivided highways, particularly where slow-moving truck traffic represents a high percentage of total road traffic. In addition, various traffic flow studies have shown that as highway operating speeds are increased wider pavements are usually required to reduce the "skin friction" between opposing and passing streams of traffic. Thus, in addition to increasing sight distance requirements, increases in the design speed of a road facility generally produce increases in total road width, with corresponding increases in all the construction cost elements shown in Table 3.1. Design speed also affects allowable curvature. In hilly or mountainous terrain, reductions in allowable curvature can lead to large increases in earthwork quantities. Finally, increasing design speed limits maximum allowable gradients, thereby introducing further earthwork costs in all but flat terrain.[1]

Among the states of nature shown in Table 3.1, terrain and geological considerations are the most important factors to be considered. Terrain conditions determine the quantities of earthwork necessary to construct a road to any given standards in a given area; geological factors determine the cost of excavating these quantities as well as the time required to complete the excavation.[2] In analyzing the effect of changes in design standards on construction costs, then, separate analyses should be made for different categories of terrain and geological conditions.

Ideally, variation in highway construction costs with changes in design standards could be analyzed by selecting certain already completed roads, changing their design standards, and

[1] These relationships are described exactly in practically any text on highway design. See, for example, Clarkson H. Oglesby and Laurence I. Hewes, *Highway Engineering*, Second Edition (New York: John Wiley & Sons, Inc., 1964), Chapters 8 and 9.

[2] The relationships between geology and excavation requirements for highway construction in Venezuela are described by Oswaldo de Sola, "Necesidad de Una Definición Mecánica de las Rocas Para los Estúdios Geológicos de Carreteras," *Boletín de Mecánica del Suelo e Ingeniería de Fundaciones* (March, 1962), pp. 3–8 (Caracas).

making estimates of the construction costs corresponding to these new designs. In practice, however, such a procedure is difficult to carry out because changing design standards often means that new location surveys would be necessary. Characteristically, the preliminary location of a new highway is located on small-scale maps with certain design standards already in mind. Detailed surveys are then made in a narrow band about this center line, permitting relatively small variations to be made in the final location of the line (usually only with respect to the profile or vertical alignment). Within this band, only slight variations in standards can be made (except in very flat terrain) as any great changes would mean that the original preliminary band was no longer best for the new design standards. Thus, to effect major changes in design standards, a much larger area than is customarily the case would have to be surveyed in detail.

As an alternative, various road construction projects that had been completed in Venezuela were classified according to terrain and geological factors. Within each classification, attempts were then made to develop regression equations describing the relationship between construction costs and the design standards to which each road was constructed.

One of the more difficult problems encountered in analyzing variation in construction costs in this manner concerns terrain classification. Such measures as flat, rolling, and mountainous terrain are used, but within each category variation can be considerable.[3] Moreover, a particular section of highway for which cost data are available often traverses more than one type of terrain and several types of soil. In some of the examples used in this study, cost data were available for sections as long as 50 kilometers passing through a variety of soil, terrain, and geological conditions. Classifications of terrain that are too narrow, however, may seriously restrict utilization of

[3] Terrain is often classified as flat, rolling, or mountainous for average gradient ranges of 0–1%, 1–6%, and greater than 6%, respectively. See, for example, Robert F. Baker, Robert Chieruzzi, and Richard W. Bletzacher, *Highway Costs and Their Relationship to Vehicle Size*, Bulletin 168, Engineering Experiment Station (Columbus: Ohio State University, 1958), p. 95.

the available data; the entire data sample may just not be large enough to be separated into very many groups, even though the data may be representative of a large variation in terrain conditions. This is particularly true in developing regions where the road network is not yet very dense. Attempts to classify terrain more rigorously had to be abandoned because of the small sample size relegated to each classification.[4]

In the analysis of Venezuelan road construction costs, sufficient data were not available to consider separately the variation of each cost element for changes in design standards. All costs of construction, exclusive of pavement costs, were therefore grouped together. Because of the difficulties of classifying terrain, only two classifications were used—*llanos,* which includes flat and gently rolling terrain, and mountain regions.

The major design variables that were taken into account were road width and design speed. The use of design speed implicitly takes into account the remaining standards that have significant effects on road construction costs (i.e., sight distances, curvature, and gradient).

Construction cost data were obtained from an analysis of approximately 2,100 kilometers of road constructed in Venezuela prior to 1960. In some cases, cost data were available on a per kilometer basis, showing each of the component costs and even the division of these costs between labor, imported materials, and depreciation of equipment. In other cases, cost data were expressed as lump sum figures for sections of road ranging up to 50 kilometers in length.

In Venezuela, four types of two-lane highways (A, B, C, and D) are now in use, differing primarily with respect to design speed, pavement width, and width of shoulders.[5] Ex-

[4] The method of terrain classification attempted here made use of the ratio of grade-line to straight-line distance, calculated at some arbitrary level, such as 3%. By picking two points on the proposed highway alignment, the shortest route that at no point exceeded gradients of 3% could be determined and compared to the straight-line distance between the points. High ratios would correspond to difficult terrain, and terrain could be classified according to this index.

[5] Road widths of 21.3, 14.6, 10.3 and 7.2 meters and design speeds of 100, 80, 60 and 50 kilometers per hour are usual for type A, B, C, and D roads, respectively, in flat terrain.

amples of actual roads constructed corresponding to each of these road types could not always be found for both types of terrain considered. (Type A roads are generally rare in mountainous regions.) Therefore, in cases where actual data pertaining to a particular road type were lacking, it was necessary to use construction cost estimates prepared by the Ministry of Public Works.

For each project considered, three types of data were obtained: total construction costs per kilometer, average design width (since widths sometimes varied in a single project), and average design speed. Linear multiple regression analysis was used to obtain construction cost equations for the two types of terrain considered. The resultant equations are[6]

$$C_L = 5720W + 3830V - 123,000 \qquad (3.1)$$

and

$$C_M = 57,900W + 5860V - 490,000 \qquad (3.2)$$

where

$C_L, C_M =$ cost per kilometer in bolivars for flat and mountainous terrain, respectively,[7]

$W =$ design width in meters

$V =$ design speed in kilometers per hour.

Least-squares curve fits were also made with respect to design speed. In this case, costs per kilometer were expressed per unit of road width. The equations are

$$C_L' = 256V + 1022 \qquad (3.3)$$
$$C_M' = 985V - 4920 \qquad (3.4)$$

where

$C_L', C_M' =$ cost per kilometer in bolivars per meter of road width.

---

[6] Coefficients of these equations have been rounded in order to reduce them to the appropriate number of significant figures. For the two equations, R^2 of 0.97 and 0.96 respectively were obtained.

[7] $1.00 U.S. = 4.48 bolivars.

The least-squares equations are plotted in Figure 3.2.

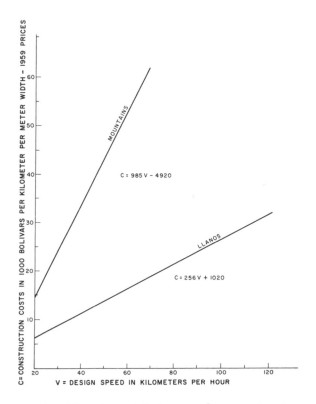

FIGURE 3.2. *The effect of design speed on construction costs.*

Estimates of the relative importance of the various construction cost elements were also made from the cost data available on a more detailed basis. These are shown in Table 3.2 for llanos and mountainous terrain. Labor, fuel, domestic materials, imported materials, and depreciation components of these cost elements are shown in Table 3.3. These cost distributions are based on averages of all road types. Estimates of labor, local currency, and foreign exchange components for changes in road width were also made as shown in Table 3.4.[8] Even in

[8] Methods of arriving at these estimates are discussed in Appendix A (p. 129).

Table 3.2.   Relative Importance of Road Cost
Elements in Venezuela

Cost Elements	Llanos Terrain	Mountainous Terrain
Preparation of Site	7.0%	6.0%
Earthwork	37.2	48.6
Culverts and Drainage	16.0	12.9
Base	7.7	10.2
Bridges	30.1	20.8
Fencing	2.0	1.5
Total	100.0	100.0

Source: Construction projects obtained from the Ministerio de Obras Públicas, Caracas.

view of the limitations on data accuracy, these distributions remain remarkably constant with labor, local capital, and foreign exchange accounting for 27, 44, and 29% of total construction costs, respectively. These distributions can be used in conjunction with the regression equations developed previously to estimate labor and capital cost variations with changes in design standards.

Design Standards and Pavement Costs

One of the main problems encountered in analyzing pavement costs stems from the variety of different methods which exist for the design of highway pavements. Under similar soil conditions, axle load, and traffic volume, these methods can lead to widely differing designs and associated costs.[9] Such discrepancies occur because present methods of pavement

[9] For example, in designing a flexible pavement to support an 8.5 metric-ton axle load on a fairly good subgrade (California Bearing Ratio, CBR, value of 10), various design methods lead to pavement thicknesses ranging from 13 to 30 cm. See Robert F. Baker and Emmett H. Karrer, *A Study of the Relationship of Pavement Cost to Vehicle Weight*, Bulletin 161, Engineering Experiment Station (Columbus: Ohio State University, 1956), p. 30.

Table 3.3. Labor, Local Capital, and Foreign Exchange Components of Road Cost Elements

Cost Elements	Detailed Breakdown in %							Aggregate Figures in %[2]			
	(1)	(2)	(3)	(4)	(5)	(6)	(7)				
	Labor[1]	Profits	Domestic Materials	Imported Materials	Fuels	Depreciation and General Expenses	Total	Labor	Local Capital	Foreign Exchange	Total
Preparation of Site	28.2	10.4	—	22.0	7.1	32.3	100.0	28.2	33.6	38.2	100.0
Earthwork	28.8	10.7	—	25.1	5.8	29.6	100.0	28.8	31.3	39.9	100.0
Culverts and Drainage	17.7	10.7	50.8	13.9	0.4	6.5	100.0	17.7	65.2	17.1	100.0
Base	29.7	10.7	12.0	20.0	3.9	23.7	100.0	29.7	38.5	31.8	100.0
Bridges	28.4	10.7	33.8	13.4	0.7	13.0	100.0	28.4	51.7	19.9	100.0
Fencing	24.3	10.7	65.0	—	—	—	100.0	24.3	75.7	—	100.0

1 Includes 30% social benefits.
2 Derived from the detailed breakdown as follows:
Labor = Column (1)
Local Capital = Columns (2) + (3) + (5) + 50% of Column (6)
Foreign Exchange = Column (4) + 50% of Column (6)

Source: Construction projects obtained from the Ministerio de Obras Públicas, Caracas. *Calculated at 1959 prices.*

Table 3.4. Estimated Labor, Local Capital, and Foreign Exchange Components of Road Construction Costs for Various Road Widths (*in per cent*)

Cost Component	Road Width in Meters			
	7.2	*10.3*	*14.6*	*21.3*
Labor	27.3	26.8	26.5	26.3
Local Capital	44.2	44.5	44.6	44.8
Foreign Exchange	28.5	28.7	28.9	28.9
Total	100.0	100.0	100.0	100.0

design are largely empirical. They are based on performance characteristics of pavements constructed in the past and thus depend to a great extent on local conditions.

The two major types of highway pavements are rigid and flexible pavements. These differ primarily in the manner in which they distribute loads applied at the surface to the subgrade below. A rigid pavement consists of a relatively thin concrete slab that, due to its rigidity, spreads the applied load over a relatively wide area of soil. Most of the load is carried by the structural capacity of the slab itself, while the remainder is reduced by the spreading characteristics of the design to stress levels that can be safely carried by the subgrade. Flexible pavements, on the other hand, consist of a series of layers of progressively higher quality materials. The top layer or wearing surface is usually asphalt. The thickness of these layers depends primarily on the strength of the subgrade. To a much greater extent, therefore, flexible pavement designs depend upon the characteristics of the soil over which the road is constructed.[10]

Flexible pavements are particularly well adapted to developing regions because of their suitability for stage construction. Where traffic volumes and axle loads are uncertain, thin pave-

[10] For a more detailed description, see E. J. Yoder, *Principles of Pavement Design* (New York: John Wiley & Sons, Inc., 1959), pp. 4–6.

47

ments can be provided initially. As traffic increases, additional layers of pavement can be added with little loss of the investment already made in the underlying pavement. Where roads traverse a wide variety of soil conditions, flexible pavements take better advantage of good soil conditions as well as the availability of good road-making materials. (On the other hand, where there is a shortage of good road-making materials, rigid pavements may be preferable.) In Venezuela, flexible pavements are also more common because of the availability of asphalt as a petroleum by-product.

Pavement thickness and hence pavement costs depend basically on the axle load for which the pavement is to be designed, the characteristics of the subgrade soil, and the volume and composition of the future traffic anticipated. The heavier the axle load, the greater will be the pavement thickness required to distribute this load in such a fashion that the resulting subgrade deflections will not be excessive.[11] Load frequency is also an important design factor because of pavement fatigue; a large number of small loads can be as damaging as a smaller number of large loads.

The method of flexible pavement design used in Venezuela is that recommended by the Asphalt Institute.[12] It takes into account axle loads, subgrade strength, and some measure of traffic frequency, being sensitive to changes in traffic volumes at low levels only. This method has been used here to design flexible pavements for average soil conditions found in Venezuela (CBR of 10%) for a standard axle load of 8.5 metric

[11] Actually tire pressure and not axle load is the important factor since it is the pressure that the subgrade can withstand that determines the necessary pavement thickness. As tire pressures used on most heavy trucks are fairly constant, design methods are usually stated in terms of axle load.

Nevertheless, research on low tire pressure vehicles for underdeveloped areas is needed. Such vehicles could greatly reduce the capital investment needed in road facilities because of less stringent pavement requirements and because of their adaptability to difficult terrain without considerable earthwork. These savings would, of course, be made at the expense of increased operating costs, particularly fuel, and reduced speeds.

[12] *The Asphalt Handbook* (College Park, Maryland: Asphalt Institute, 1961), or Yoder, *op. cit.*, p. 148.

tons[13] and for several levels of traffic intensity. Some modifications to the Asphalt Institute method of accounting for traffic volumes have been made by interpolating for values between the standard traffic classifications. On the basis of these designs and unit costs obtained for pavement construction,[14] the variation in total pavement costs per kilometer for changes in design width and traffic volume can be shown as in Figure 3.3.

As in the case of construction costs, estimates were made of the various labor, capital, and energy components of total pavement costs, based on recent Venezuelan experience. These cost distributions are summarized in Table 3.5.

Table 3.5. Labor, Local Capital, and Foreign Exchange
Components of Asphalt Pavement Costs

Labor	24.3
Local	57.4
Foreign Exchange	18.3
Total	100.0

Capacity Costs

Our major concern in developing the highway construction and pavement cost relationships discussed in the preceding section is to relate these costs to highway capacity. Unit fixed costs can then be computed for various levels of transportation output.

---

[13] Designs for other axle loads could also be considered. It is one thing, however, to consider allowable axle loads in designing a road system from the beginning and quite another to consider changing the allowable axle load for a well-established road system. In the Venezuelan case, there would appear to be little justification for lowering the legal axle load where an extensive network of roads has already been designed to carry an 8.5 metric-ton load. On the other hand, to increase the legal limit would require substantial expense to strengthen the existing system when available funds could probably be used to better advantage in extending the network.

[14] Pavement costs in bolivars per square meter for varying thicknesses were obtained from Antonio Boccalandro, Jr., of Urbanismo y Vialidad, a consulting firm in Caracas which has done considerable highway design work in Venezuela.

49

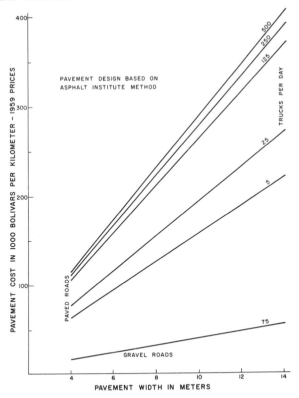

FIGURE 3.3.   *The effect of traffic volume and design width on pavement costs.*

Although highway capacity has been the subject of study for many years, no precise relationships have been developed relating the total tonnage that can be moved over a section of road to the characteristics of the road itself. Road capacity is influenced by both the physical characteristics of the road and the characteristics of the traffic using the road. Environmental factors such as weather and the nature of adjacent land use also affect capacity.

Physical factors that affect highway capacity include lane width, clearance from side obstructions, geometry of the alignment (particularly gradient and passing sight distances), and terrain. All these factors influence capacity through their effects on vehicle speed. Lane width and clearance produce similar effects; as friction between opposing lanes of traffic on two-lane roads is reduced by widening traffic lanes, vehicles tend to increase average speeds, thereby improving the capacity of each lane. In a similar manner, increasing shoulder width reduces friction with side obstructions and also increases capacity. Greater sight distances affect capacity in that they provide passing opportunities and increase the use of road sections in front of slow-moving vehicles. Gradient effects are more pronounced with respect to heavy truck traffic.

Traffic flow characteristics that affect road capacity are largely the composition of the vehicle fleet which uses the facility (particularly the ratio of heavy truck to automobile traffic), and the manner in which this traffic flow is distributed over various hours of the day. Vehicle fleet composition affects capacity because high proportions of truck traffic tend to reduce over-all average speeds and passing opportunities. Traffic flow characteristics, however, such as peaking, affect the capacity utilization and not the capacity of a road. The former represents what the road *does* produce; the latter, what it *could* produce. Thus, in cases where 15% of the average daily traffic (ADT) occurs in the peak hour, it is the capacity utilization and not the capacity itself that is lower than if the peak hour accounted for 10% of the ADT.

Methods of evaluating highway capacity have been developed that take into account many of these factors by comparing actual road and traffic characteristics with an idealized situation and applying correction factors to the capacity of the former.[15] Idealized conditions for two-lane rural highways, for example, are generally 3.65-meter lane widths (12.0 feet), 1.82-meter shoulder widths (6.0 feet), and 100% automobile traffic. If lane widths are reduced to 3.35 or 3.05 meters, lane capacity is assumed to be reduced by 14% and 23%, respectively.

[15] These methods, developed by the American Association of State Highway Officials in their *Policy on Geometric Design of Rural Highways* (Washington, 1953), are described using metric units of measurement in Comisión de Normas, *Normas Para el Proyecto de Carreteras* (Caracas: Ministerio de Obras Públicas, 1962).

51

Using these methods, estimates of highway capacity in llanos terrain have been made, assuming the proportion of trucks to be 20% of total traffic during the peak hour. In Table 3.6, hourly truck volumes are shown for various combinations

Table 3.6. The Effect of Road Width on the Capacity of Paved Roads

Lane Width in Meters	Shoulder Width in Meters	Total Meters	Hourly Capacity as % of Standard[1]	Daily Capacity in Trucks/Day[2]
3.65	1.82	10.94	100	1000
	1.22	9.74	92	920
	0.61	8.52	81	810
	0.00	7.30	70	700
3.35	1.82	10.34	86	860
	1.22	9.14	79	790
	0.61	7.92	70	700
	0.00	6.70	60	600
3.05	1.82	9.74	77	770
	1.22	8.54	71	710
	0.61	7.32	63	630
	0.00	6.10	54	540
2.75	1.82	9.14	70	700
	1.22	7.94	65	650
	0.61	6.72	57	570
	0.00	5.50	49	490

[1] Standard Hourly Capacity in rolling terrain with 20% trucks is 500 vehicles for 3.65-meter lanes and 1.82-meter shoulders. Comisión de Normas, *Normas Para el Proyecto de Carreteras* (Caracas: Ministerio de Obras Públicas, 1962), pp. 38–40.
[2] Assumes 10% of average daily truck traffic occurs in peak hour.

of lane and shoulder width. Although total peak-hour traffic is assumed to be 15.7% of average daily traffic in Venezuela, 10% has been assumed in the case of truck traffic, which should display less peaking. This results in an average of 25% truck traffic for over-all daily traffic, corresponding to past experience in Venezuela. On the basis of the peak-hour factor, annual tonnages per kilometer can be estimated for various combinations of truck size and utilization.

The data shown in Table 3.6 indicate that the hourly capacity of a road can be changed by varying the combination of lane and shoulder widths. The width of lanes and shoulders, however, is a major determinant of road construction costs. Lane widths, in addition, determine pavement costs. Total construction plus pavement costs can, therefore, be related to the design hourly capacity of the highway by applying the unit pavement costs and regression equations for construction costs to widths corresponding to the various capacity levels. Using the cost distributions described earlier, these construction and pavement costs can then be separated into their labor and capital components. Variation of these components as well as variations in total construction and pavement costs with changes in road capacity are shown in Figure 3.4.

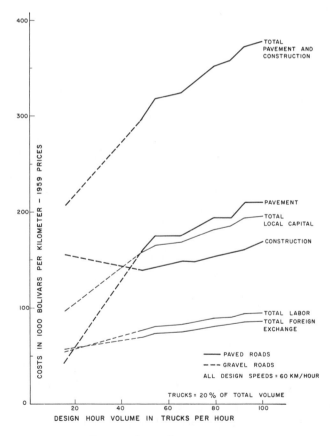

FIGURE 3.4. *Capacity costs.*

In Figure 3.4, highway capacity has been expressed in terms of heavy trucks per hour, assuming heavy truck traffic to be 20% of total traffic during the peak hour. By expressing capacity in this manner, the cost curves retain their generality. Tonnage estimates can always be made by converting these hourly capacities using the formula

$$Q = VTl/k \tag{3.5}$$

where

Q = average daily two-way capacity in ton-km/km
V = two-way truck capacity in trucks per hour
T = average truck load capacity in tons
l = load factor or percentage utilization of truck capacity
k = ratio of peak hour truck traffic to average daily truck traffic.

Thus, for various average truck sizes, utilization, and peaking characteristics, the horizontal scale of Figure 3.4 can be rescaled to give capacity in hourly, daily, or yearly tonnages. In addition, of course, capacity to accommodate automobiles and other light vehicles can also be taken into account.

The relationship between costs, capacity, and road geometry shows that considerable flexibility exists in providing road capacity even though the capacity function does display a certain degree of indivisibility.[16] Only improvements in capacity that can be obtained by widening pavements and shoulders have been considered here. Improvements such as grade reduction, increases in average sight distances, widening on steep grades, and reduction in horizontal curvature, are other methods of reducing the step function characteristics generally attributed to the highway cost-capacity function.

[16] In point of fact, what indivisibility or lumpiness does exist relates to increases in capacity and not increases in cost. A small increase in the width of a road consisting of three 3.5-meter lanes, for example, permits conversion to four 2.75-meter lanes. The two-way capacity of the road would be more than doubled. Thus for a very small increase in road width and construction cost, a very large increase in capacity would be obtained.

PART II. CURRENT COSTS

Road Maintenance Costs

Because of the variety of factors that influence the pattern of maintenance costs for various road types, maintenance data are by far the most difficult data to obtain in any analysis of road transportation costs. Traffic intensity, terrain conditions, vegetation, and climatic factors, such as rainfall and temperature differentials, all influence the maintenance needs of a road facility. In addition, the difficulty of isolating maintenance costs from those expenditures that represent capital improvements further hinders the acquisition of reliable maintenance data. This is particularly true in the case of resurfacing old pavements and in reconstructing low-cost penetration roads where equipment charged to the maintenance account is often used to provide a definite improvement in the over-all quality of the road.

Road maintenance costs are comprised of fixed and variable components. Fixed components are those that are largely independent of traffic intensity. They result from the deterioration of highway surfaces and structures caused primarily by climatic factors and the invasion of road margins by vegetation. In tropical climates, rainfall is probably the most important climatic factor, particularly where wet and dry seasons are very distinct. During the rainy season, the cost of maintaining earth and gravel roads becomes so high that it is often cheaper to pave the road surface even where traffic volumes are very low. Variable maintenance costs, on the other hand, depend primarily on traffic intensity and the frequency of heavy trucks. In general, the relative importance of fixed costs increases as one moves from earth to gravel to paved roads, whereas variable costs decrease in importance.

In order to arrive at some estimate of maintenance cost variation for different road types, statistical information on annual maintenance expenditures was combined with certain information available from the literature.[17] Using data available

[17] For example, E. K. Hawkins, *Roads and Road Transport in an Underdeveloped Country, A Case Study of Uganda* (London: Her Majesty's Station-

from the Ministry of Public Works an attempt was made to relate total maintenance expenditures, by state, with the total length of paved, gravel, and earth roads in each state. Maintenance cost equations thus derived are as follows:

$$M_P = 10,400 + 1(ADT) \tag{3.6}$$
$$M_G = 5,200 + 18(ADT) \tag{3.7}$$
$$M_E = 1,550 + 54(ADT) \tag{3.8}$$

where

$M_P =$ annual cost of maintaining paved roads in bolivars per kilometer (Bs/km)

$M_G =$ annual cost of maintaining gravel roads in Bs/km

$M_E =$ annual cost of maintaining earth roads in Bs/km

$ADT =$ average daily traffic.

These equations should be regarded as rough approximations only. Therefore, no attempt has been made to take into account differences in road standards within the paved, gravel, and earth categories used here. Within each of these categories some variation in annual maintenance costs can be expected. In general, however, differences in design standards will not produce significant differences in the pattern of maintenance costs over the life of the road. For example, loads applied near the edge of a pavement produce more distress in pavements and shoulders than loads applied nearer to the centerline. Therefore, although the area to be maintained per kilometer increases as widths are increased, the relative frequency of edge loadings decreases and tends to offset increases in maintenance costs. For small increments of width (i.e., less than a

---

ery Office, 1962), p. 154, estimates fixed maintenance costs of gravel roads to be one-half those of paved roads. Other maintenance cost data are available in Paul Bourrières, *L'Economie des Transports dans les Programmes de Développement* (Paris: Presses Universitaires de France, 1961), p. 102 ff. and Sergio Sánchez Naranjo, *El Desarrollo Económico de La Región Suroriental y Los Transportes* (Caracas: Corporación Venezolana de Guayana, División de Estúdios, Planificación e Investigación, January 1962), pp. 64–65.

lane) maintenance costs will be unaffected because the length of road for which each road gang is responsible does not change. In other words, total costs remain roughly the same and the productivity of the maintenance crew is forced to increase or, alternatively, the quality of maintenance may decline.

Equations 3.6 through 3.8 lead to high annual maintenance costs. In 1959 and 1960, average road maintenance costs in Venezuela for all road types were Bs 9,000 and Bs 12,000 per kilometer, respectively.[18] In the United States, on the other hand, where traffic intensity is generally much greater, estimates of annual maintenance costs for two-lane paved roads range around $250 per mile for the surface only.[19] Allowing an additional $600 for other maintenance brings the total to approximately Bs 2,400 per kilometer. Maintenance costs are thus considerably higher in Venezuela than in the United States. Some of the reasons for these high cost characteristics, which extend to road construction as well as maintenance, have been discussed elsewhere.[20] Road maintenance, however, generally tends to be a labor-intensive process. Of over-all road maintenance expenditures in Venezuela during the period 1960–1962, approximately 76% was for salaries, wages, and workers benefits. Local materials and capital accounted for an addi-

[18] Source: Ministerio de Obras Públicas, Dirección de Ejecución. In their benefit-cost analyses of road improvements, the World Bank mission to Venezuela used estimates of road maintenance costs reported to be representative of Venezuelan conditions. These estimates could not be verified by this writer and, in general, seem to understate actual costs by a considerable amount. See International Bank for Reconstruction and Development, *The Economic Development of Venezuela* (Baltimore: The Johns Hopkins Press, 1961), pp. 449–50.

[19] *Economics of Asphalt and Concrete for Highway Construction* (Menlo Park, California: Stanford Research Institute, 1961), p. 5.

[20] The World Bank mission attributes these costs to administrative deficiencies (such as an unnecessary number of clerks and accountants) and the fact that the labor component of maintenance costs is still very large despite the capital-intensive techniques employed. The mission also feels that the government policy of using its own forces rather than contract forces further contributes to the high cost of highway maintenance. International Bank, *op. cit.*, pp. 253–254, 257–258.

tional 16%, while the remaining 8% of total maintenance costs was comprised of imports. In view of earlier discussions on accounting versus market prices, the real costs of road maintenance in Venezuela would thus be considerably lower than the figures indicate.

The relatively short treatment given here to road maintenance is in no way indicative of the importance to be attached to the subject. The way in which the pattern of road maintenance requirements varies for roads constructed to different standards, under varying levels of traffic volumes, and under different climatic conditions, is one of the most important areas to be studied in analyzing the transportation needs of developing regions. In addition to extending the life of the capital investment already in the road, expenditures on road maintenance can be as important in extending the life of vehicles using the facility as private outlays made by the vehicle owners themselves.[21] The brevity of this treatment only emphasizes the general lack of relevant maintenance cost data.

Design Standards and Vehicle Operating Costs

Costs of motor vehicle operation can also be divided into two groups: those costs that are fixed or independent of the degree to which the vehicle is used, and those costs that are variable or dependent upon vehicle use. In the former category fall such costs as depreciation due to obsolescence, insurance, taxes and licenses, and garaging. Because the life of a vehicle is relatively short compared to the life of road facilities, these fixed costs can be considered as short-run fixed costs. Among variable costs the most important are depreciation due to wear, fuel, maintenance, and wages paid to drivers and their helpers.

In the design of transport systems we are interested only in those elements of vehicle operation that can be affected by changes in system design. Normally, this excludes most of the

[21] Gilbert Walker, *Traffic and Transport in Nigeria, The Example of an Underdeveloped Tropical Territory* (London: Her Majesty's Stationery Office, 1959), p. ix.

elements of fixed costs. In underdeveloped regions, however, changes in system design can often have serious effects on unit fixed charges by (a) increasing the useful lives of vehicles through improvements to road surfaces and alignment, and (b) improving the utilization of vehicles through over-all increases in average running speeds. Therefore, both fixed and variable motor vehicle operating costs are considered.

Fixed operating costs. The most important fixed cost of vehicle operation is the initial cost of acquiring the vehicle. This initial cost depends primarily upon the size and type of the vehicle (whether single or multiple unit and the number of axles) as well as upon such characteristics as power-weight ratios, engine type, and any special characteristics of the body design.

Although single-unit vehicles are the predominant type to be found in Venezuela today, these generally are not used extensively for line-haul freight operations once a reasonable degree of traffic volume materializes. With sufficient traffic volumes, multiple-unit trucks permit greater use of power units since additional trailers may be purchased with each truck-trailer combination. This permits power units to be used for line-haul operation, while trailers left with shippers or consignees are being loaded or unloaded. With single-unit vehicles, the power unit must remain idle during the loading operation, resulting in correspondingly lower rates of equipment utilization.

Representative initial costs of combination trucks, ranging in capacity from 7.9 to 23.5 metric tons, are shown in Table 3.7. These costs are for trucks landed in Venezuela and do not include any Venezuelan taxes or import duties. An allowance of 15% has been made to cover the costs of shipment to Venezuela from the United States. Prices are exclusive of tires since these are considered to be variable costs. Table 3.7 also shows the ratio of payload to gross vehicle weight and gives some indication of the capital investment per unit capacity.

In calculating depreciation and interest charges on a unit basis, it is necessary to know the economic life of the vehicle

Table 3.7. Representative Cost and Weight Data
for Combination Trucks

Item	Semi-trailer	Semi-trailer	Semi-trailer	Semi-trailer	Semi- and Full trailer
Axle Classification	2-S1	2-S1	2-S2	3-S2	2-S1-2
Number of Tires	10	10	14	18	18
Weights (metric tons)					
Power unit	2.6	3.8	4.7	6.5	5.4
Trailer(s)	3.0	3.6	4.9	5.1	7.4
Total Tare Weight	5.6	7.4	9.6	11.6	12.8
Payload	7.8	11.4	15.9	21.0	23.5
Gross Combination Weight (GCW)	13.4	18.8	25.5	32.6	36.3
Engine Type	gasoline	gasoline	gasoline	diesel	diesel
Horsepower	132	156	184	216	230
HP/ton	9.8	8.3	7.2	6.6	6.3
Prices (1959 bolivars)					
Power unit	18,300	31,600	47,300	94,000	86,400
Trailer(s)	18,300	20,500	26,000	28,100	48,400
Total	36,600	52,100	73,300	122,100	134,800
Bolivars/ton of Payload	4,690	4,580	4,610	5,810	5,730
Ratio of Payload/GCW	.58	.61	.62	.64	.65

and the appropriate rate of interest to be used in determining annual capital charges. Generally, depreciation of a capital asset results from its physical deterioration through usage and obsolescence that takes place over time. In the case of trucks used for line-haul freight transportation, however, obsolescence is a relatively unimportant factor. Trucks are normally driven until maintenance costs become so excessive as to make replacement by a new vehicle more economical. The economic life of the vehicle thus depends upon the total number of kilometers over which the vehicle can operate economically and the factors that influence its average annual utilization. Annual capital charges, then, are given by the equation:

$$D = \text{CRF}_{i,n} (I - S) + Si \qquad (3.10)$$

where

D = annual debt service

$\mathrm{CRF}_{i,n}$ = capital recovery factor for interest rate i and life $n =$
    K/k

  K = total kilometers that can be obtained from the vehicle

  k = average annual kilometers

  I = initial cost of vehicle

  S = salvage value.

By the definition of depreciation that we have been using here, the salvage value of the truck would be limited to its scrap value. This is sometimes taken as 1% of the initial cost,[22] and no great error will be introduced by neglecting it. If we rewrite Equation 3.9, unit debt service charges are given by

$$d = \mathrm{CRF}_{i,n}\,(I)/k \qquad\qquad (3.10)$$

in bolivars per vehicle-kilometer.

Determination of n (or K), of course, is not an easy matter since it requires knowing how truck maintenance costs vary as the distance traveled by the vehicle increases. This can be illustrated graphically as in Figure 3.5. As the life of the vehicle increases (or as the total kilometers are increased while the yearly average remains constant), annual capital charges decrease. Equivalent annual maintenance costs,[23] however, would increase as greater and greater effort is required to keep the vehicle in running order. The useful economic life of the truck is given where the sum of these two costs, as shown by the total cost curve, is a minimum. Obviously the location of this minimum point depends upon the rate of interest.

The pattern of maintenance costs, as described by the curve of Figure 3.5, and hence the economic life depends upon such factors as road conditions, terrain, average vehicle speed, average loadings, and maintenance procedures. In practice, such curves describing the pattern of maintenance costs are almost

---

[22] *Line-Haul Trucking Costs in Relation to Vehicle Gross Weights,* Bulletin 301 (Washington: Highway Research Board, 1961), p. 72 (HRB 301).

[23] Note that future maintenance costs must again be discounted in calculating average annual maintenance costs.

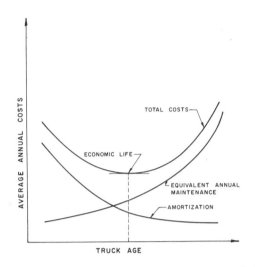

FIGURE 3.5. *Determination of economic truck life.*

impossible to obtain, and very subjective evaluations are often used to determine just when a vehicle has outlived its useful economic life. Under Venezuelan conditions, estimates of useful truck life range from 550,000 to 650,000 kilometers[24] for trucks of approximately 10-ton capacity operating on paved surfaces. For larger trucks, particularly diesel-powered trucks, some increase in useful life can be expected. In Table 3.8, the effects of the variations in vehicle life on unit depreciation charges are shown for several rates of interest.

On unpaved surfaces both vehicle life and annual utilization will be considerably less than on paved surfaces. Very little data are available, however, to indicate the magnitude of the differences between operation on paved and unpaved surfaces.[25] In Uganda, truck owners indicated that depreciation

[24] International Bank, *op. cit.*, p. 458. The latter figure corresponds to American trucking experience as in HRB 301, *op. cit.*, pp. 73–75.

[25] Bourrières, *op. cit.*, p. 98, estimates total vehicle operating costs (including fixed and variable costs) on unpaved surfaces to be twice as high as on paved surfaces, while Robley Winnfrey, "Highway Economics" in *Highway Engineering Handbook*, Kenneth B. Woods, ed. (New York: McGraw Hill, 1960), pp. 3–32, estimates a 15% differential for operation on unpaved surfaces.

Table 3.8.   The Effect of Vehicle Life and Interest Rate on
Interest and Depreciation Charges per Vehicle-
kilometers. Operation on Paved Surfaces

Items[1]	Truck Capacity in Metric Tons				
	7.8	11.4	15.9	21.0	23.5
Total Initial Value (bolivars)[2]	47,600	64,400	88,900	139,000	163,800
Low Life[3] (1000 km)	550	550	610	780	780
Depreciation plus interest[4] in Bs/veh-km at					
8%	.0975	.1350	.1800	.2450	.2990
10%	.1040	.1430	.1910	.2710	.3210
12%	.1100	.1510	.2020	.2870	.3410
15%	.1180	.1640	.2190	.3140	.3720
High Life[3] (1000 km)	650	650	720	920	920
Depreciation plus interest[4] in Bs/veh-km at					
8%	.0925	.1260	.1690	.2270	.2830
10%	.0985	.1340	.1790	.2590	.3040
12%	.1040	.1420	.1910	.2680	.3170
15%	.1140	.1540	.2070	.2950	.3540

[1] Costs in 1959 bolivars.
[2] Assumes 1.6 trailers per power unit.
[3] Trailer life assumed constant at 9 years.
[4] Assumes 80,000 kilometers per year.

charges were reduced from 60 to 70% as a result of shifting
from operation on unpaved to paved surfaces.[26] For purposes
of the present study, depreciation charges are assumed to be
50% higher on unpaved surfaces, and annual vehicle utilization reduced from 80,000 to 50,000 kilometers.

[26] Hawkins, op. cit., p. 164.

63

In addition to annual capital charges on equipment, there are fixed charges for taxes, licenses, and vehicle insurance. Taxes and license fees are not considered here. To the extent that such charges represent an attempt to recoup investments in highway facilities, including them would involve a considerable degree of double counting since the costs of constructing such facilities has already been taken into account.

Insurance costs depend primarily on vehicle size and value. In principle, they should be equivalent to the expected value of accident costs over the life of the vehicle. Consequently, heavier vehicles that cause greater damage in a collision incur correspondingly higher liability premiums; collision premiums will also be higher because of the greater cost of the large vehicles. In Table 3.9, insurance costs for liability have been based on interpolations for quotations on 10- and 15-ton vehicles. Collision premiums have been computed on the basis of 6% of truck value that, on the average, will be one-half the initial cost. Personal and merchandise insurance costs are largely independent of vehicle size.

Variable operating costs. One of the most difficult undertakings in any study of transportation economics concerns the determination of representative variable operating costs for trucks of different sizes operating over various types of road under different terrain conditions. Because a truck usually operates under a variety of conditions during its useful life, it is often difficult to trace certain elements of cost back to particular conditions of operation. In developing countries the difficulty of obtaining representative cost information is often further aggravated by the lack of uniform (or mandatory) accounting procedures among common carriers such as are enforced in the United States by the Interstate Commerce Commission. Even where firms do keep detailed accounts of their operating expenditures, they are generally reluctant to divulge any of this information.

During the 1930's considerable attention was focused around the effects of road surfaces and alignments on costs of motor vehicle operation. Controlled experiments carried out by the Oregon State Highway Commission and the Iowa Engineering

Table 3.9. Summary of Truck Operating Costs (*Excluding Depreciation*) for Operation on Paved, Gravel, and Earth Roads
(*in bolivars per vehicle-kilometer*)

Cost Items[1]	Truck Capacity in Metric Tons				
	7.8	11.4	15.9	21.0	23.5
Paved Roads[2]					
Drivers[3]	0.325	0.325	0.335	0.345	0.378
Maintenance[4]	0.055	0.063	0.085	0.104	0.107
Tires[5]	0.107	0.107	0.150	0.193	0.193
Gasoline[6]	0.051	0.063	0.075	—	—
Diesel Oil[7]	—	—	—	0.021	0.023
Oil	0.010	0.016	0.022	0.025	0.025
Insurance[8]	0.036	0.042	0.050	0.069	0.075
Total	0.584	0.616	0.717	0.757	0.801
Gravel Roads[9]					
Drivers[10]	0.520	0.520	0.537	0.552	0.606
Maintenance[11] (5.6)	0.308	0.353	0.477	0.582	0.599
Tires (1.68)	0.199	0.199	0.252	0.324	0.324
Gasoline (1.15)	0.059	0.072	0.086	—	—
Diesel Oil (1.15)	—	—	—	0.024	0.026
Oil (1.51)	0.015	0.024	0.033	0.038	0.038
Insurance[10]	0.058	0.067	0.080	0.110	0.120
Total	1.159	1.235	1.465	1.630	1.713
Earth Roads[9]					
Drivers[10]	0.520	0.520	0.537	0.552	0.606
Maintenance (10.0)	0.550	0.630	0.850	1.040	1.070
Tires (1.24)	0.133	0.133	0.186	0.239	0.239
Gasoline (1.11)	0.057	0.070	0.083	—	—
Diesel Oil (1.11)	—	—	—	0.023	0.025
Oil (2.11)	0.021	0.034	0.046	0.053	0.053
Insurance[10]	0.058	0.067	0.080	0.110	0.120
Total	1.339	1.454	1.782	2.017	2.113

[1] *All costs in 1959 bolivars.*

[2] Annual truck utilization assumed to be 80,000 kilometers.

[3] Base wage of Bs 2,170 per month (including 45% benefits) increased by 3, 6, 16% respectively, for 15.9-, 21.0-, and 23.5-ton trucks.

[4] Includes engine overhaul estimate of 7.7 Bs/hp every 60,000 kilometers and monthly charges of Bs 150, 180, 300, 400, 350, respectively.

[5] Assumed tire life of 42,000 kilometers and cost of Bs 450 per tire.

[6] Average of empty and fully loaded fuel consumption computed for a rise and fall of 2.0 meters/100 meters, after Saal, *op. cit.*, p. 39, and fuel costs of Bs 0.14/liter.

[7] Fuel consumption computed as per (6) and divided by 1.52 and 1.55 for 21.0- and 23.5-ton trucks respectively, to allow for greater diesel efficiency. Fuel adjustment factors taken from U.S. Congress, *Final Report of the Highway Cost Allocation Study*, House Document No. 54 (Washington: Government Printing Office, 1961), p. 204. Diesel fuel costs assumed to be Bs 0.50 per liter.

[8] Includes an annual charge of 3% of initial value of truck for collision.

[9] Truck utilization assumed to be 50,000 kilometers/year.

[10] Annual total remains constant while utilization is reduced from 80,000 to 50,000 kilometers/year.

[11] Figures in parentheses indicate adjustment factors applied to costs of operation on paved surfaces.

Experiment Station have become classics in the field[27] and provided the basis for most benefit-cost analyses of highway improvements.[28] These studies investigated the effects of changes in design standards, such as gradient and curvature, on the operating costs of particular vehicles operating over various types of road surface. Later studies introduced more generality and allowed for greater agglomeration of individual effects. From tests carried out by the U.S. Bureau of Public Roads, for example, it is possible to relate truck fuel consumption and speeds to such general parameters as gross vehicle weight and power-weight ratio for various types of terrain.[29]

Despite their age, data obtained from these and other studies proved useful in supplementing available data on Venezuelan trucking costs. In particular, these studies were useful in determining rates of fuel consumption for the truck sizes considered here and in determining differences in costs of truck operation over earth and gravel roads. In all cases where foreign data were used, however, adjustments were made to take into account differences in unit prices, such as the price of fuel.

In Table 3.9, estimated truck operating costs have been itemized for the five trucks under consideration. Using the

[27] Of the Oregon Studies see John Beakey, *The Effect of Highway Design on Vehicle Speed and Fuel Consumption,* Technical Bulletin No. 5 (1937, reprinted 1955); C. B. McCullough and John Beakey, *The Economics of Highway Planning,* Technical Bulletin No. 7 (1937); and John Beakey and F. B. Crandall, *The Effect of Surface Type, Alignment and Traffic Congestion on Vehicular Fuel Consumption,* Technical Bulletin No. 17 (1944), all published by the Oregon State Highway Commission, Salem, Oregon. Studies published by the Iowa Engineering Experiment Station, Ames, Iowa, include R. A. Moyer and Robley Winnfrey, *Cost of Operating Rural Mail-Carrier Motor Vehicles on Pavement, Gravel, and Earth,* Bulletin 143 (1939), and R. A. Moyer and Glen L. Tesdall, *Tire Wear and Cost on Selected Roadway Surfaces,* Bulletin 131 (1945).

[28] See, for example, *Road User Benefit Analyses for Highway Improvements* (Washington: American Association of State Highway Officials, 1960), referred to as the AASHO Red Book.

[29] Carl Saal, *Time and Gasoline Consumption in Motor Truck Operation as Affected by the Weight and Power of Vehicles and the Rise and Fall in Highways,* Research Report 9-A (Washington: Highway Research Board, 1950).

basic data for paved surfaces, adjustments made for operation on unpaved earth and gravel surfaces[30] have also been included. Labor, local currency, and foreign exchange components of these operating costs for an interest rate of 10% have been estimated as shown in Table 3.10. In each case, foreign exchange components are estimated to include depreciation and 25% of maintenance costs.

The variable costs shown in Tables 3.9 and 3.10 are stated in terms of costs per vehicle-kilometer for line-haul trucking operations. In order to translate these vehicle-kilometer costs into costs per ton-kilometer, some estimate of the utilization characteristics of each truck type must be made.

The major factors which affect vehicle utilization are the magnitude and frequency of traffic volumes and the availability of return loads. The availability of return loads in turn depends upon the balance of incoming and outgoing commodity flows and the nature of the freight being carried in each direction. If outgoing traffic is largely composed of steel reinforcing bars, for example, there is little likelihood that the same trucks would obtain much of the incoming consumer goods. Smaller trucks can better afford to wait for return loads. For larger vehicles, the "economics of standing still" probably dictates that their best utilization will be obtained by returning for new loads as quickly as possible.

In general, for all but the shipment of bulk commodities, utilization will improve with decreasing vehicle size. This improvement in utilization is the basic reason why small vehicles are at all competitive since, as the figures in Table 3.9 indicate, unit costs per ton-kilometer decrease with increasing vehicle size if fully loaded vehicles are assumed. When traffic volumes become sufficient to ensure adequate use, large multiple-unit trucks enjoy a considerable cost advantage over small, single-unit vehicles.

Truck operating costs have been recalculated on a ton-

[30] Adjustments are based on data from Moyer and Winnfrey, op. cit., pp. 23, 43; Moyer and Tesdall, op. cit., p. 45; and H. D. Daftary and M. K. Ganguli, "Road Transport Operation Cost on Various Types of Surfaces," Journal of the Indian Roads Congress, XXIV, 3 (December, 1959), p. 251.

Table 3.10.   Total Truck Operating Costs on Paved, Gravel, and Earth Roads Showing Labor, Local Capital, and Foreign Exchange Components at 10% Interest
(in bolivars per vehicle-kilometer)

Items[1]	Truck Capacity in Metric Tons				
	7.8	*11.4*	*15.9*	*21.0*	*23.5*
Paved Roads					
Depreciation and Interest[2]	0.101	0.138	0.185	0.265	0.312
Other Operating Costs	0.584	0.616	0.717	0.757	0.801
Total	0.685	0.754	0.902	1.022	1.113
Labor	0.352	0.356	0.378	0.397	0.431
Local Capital	0.218	0.244	0.318	0.334	0.343
Foreign Exchange	0.115	0.154	0.206	0.291	0.339
Gravel Roads					
Depreciation and Interest[3]	0.152	0.207	0.278	0.398	0.468
Other Operating Costs	1.159	1.235	1.465	1.630	1.713
Total	1.311	1.442	1.743	2.028	2.181
Labor	0.674	0.697	0.776	0.843	0.905
Local Capital	0.408	0.450	0.570	0.642	0.658
Foreign Exchange	0.229	0.295	0.397	0.543	0.618
Earth Roads					
Depreciation and Interest[3]	0.152	0.207	0.278	0.398	0.468
Other Operating Costs	1.339	1.454	1.782	2.017	2.113
Total	1.491	1.661	2.060	2.415	2.581
Labor	0.790	0.830	0.967	1.072	1.136
Local Capital	0.409	0.464	0.605	0.685	0.707
Foreign Exchange	0.292	0.367	0.488	0.658	0.738

[1] *All costs in 1959 bolivars.*
[2] Average from Table 3.9.
[3] 50% increase over paved roads.

kilometer basis, with the load factors shown in Table 3.11. With the exception of the two smallest trucks, it was assumed that no other trucks would obtain a return load. On the outgoing trip load factors varying from 80 to 100% were assumed.

Table 3.11. Truck Operating Costs on Paved, Gravel, and Earth Roads Showing Labor, Local Capital, and Foreign Exchange Components at 10% Interest

(in bolivars per 1000 ton-kilometers)

Items[1]	Truck Capacity in Metric Tons				
	7.8	*11.4*	*15.9*	*21.0*	*23.5*
Two-Way Load Factor in per cent	70.0	55.0	50.0	42.5	40.0
Paved Roads					
Labor	64.5	56.8	47.6	44.5	45.9
Local Capital	39.9	38.9	40.0	37.4	36.5
Foreign Exchange	21.1	24.6	25.9	32.6	36.1
Total	125.5	120.3	113.5	114.5	118.5
Gravel Roads					
Labor	123.6	111.2	97.6	94.4	96.3
Local Capital	74.8	71.8	71.7	71.9	70.0
Foreign Exchange	42.0	47.0	49.9	60.8	65.8
Total	240.4	230.0	219.2	227.1	232.1
Earth Roads					
Labor	144.7	132.4	121.6	120.1	120.9
Local Capital	74.9	74.0	76.1	76.7	75.2
Foreign Exchange	53.5	58.5	61.4	73.7	78.5
Total	273.1	264.9	259.1	270.5	274.6

[1] *All costs in 1959 bolivars.*

When line-haul costs have been determined on a unit basis the remaining costs to be considered are terminal costs. These include costs of pick-up and delivery to and from the freight terminal, platform handling charges, and billing charges. On a ton-kilometer basis, these terminal costs obviously depend upon the length of line-haul since the costs per ton are independent of the distance the freight is to be moved. Terminal costs per ton depend largely on the size and nature of the shipment. Certain charges as, for example, billing charges, are independent of shipment size; therefore, costs per ton decrease for larger shipments. In addition, larger shipments are less likely to be transferred from one truck to another since the pick-up and delivery truck may also be the truck used for the line-haul, thereby eliminating platform charges altogether.[31]

Terminal costs, therefore, are basically a function of the nature of the cargo and the distance over which this cargo is to be moved. As such, they are not affected by changes in road design or by the type of vehicle to be used, nor do they influence the selection among alternative design standards. In comparing alternative techniques of production, as we have been doing here, it is only the differences between alternatives that are of interest. Since terminal costs do not affect these differences, they can be excluded from the present discussion. Terminal costs do become relevant, however, when intermodal comparisons as between railroads and roads are considered.

PART III. COMBINED FIXED AND CURRENT COSTS

The line-haul operating costs which have been developed for earth, gravel, and paved roads can be combined with costs of construction and maintenance for each of these road types to determine the variations in total line-haul costs for different levels of traffic. Total annual maintenance and operating costs can be related directly to the annual tonnage moved per kilometer through the maintenance costs equations and ton-kilometer operating costs shown in the previous part. In order to convert the costs of construction into equivalent annual cost, however, some estimate of facility life is first required.

As in the case of determining economic truck lives, facility life could theoretically be determined by analyzing the variation of annual capital charges and maintenance costs with time and determining the point at which reconstruction of the facility would be more economical than to continue to maintain it. Again, for lack of the relevant maintenance data, it is

---

[31] An excellent discussion of trucking terminal costs is to be found in John R. Meyer, Merton J. Peck, John Stenason, and Charles Zwick, *The Economics of Competition in the Transportation Industries* (Cambridge, Mass.: Harvard University Press, 1959), pp. 89–93.

usually necessary to rely upon subjective evaluations of economic road life. In the case of earth roads, facility lives of 4 to 6 years are usually assumed.[32] Although the physical life of such elements as structures is usually longer than this, new alignments are generally selected when earth roads are reconstructed. In the case of gravel roads, however, alignments are selected with greater care. When these are replaced by paved roads, the major changes that take place concern the road surface alone. The economic life of a gravel road, then, would be considerably higher than an earth road; it has been estimated here to be about 15 years. For paved roads, lives of 25 years have been assumed for all cost elements except pavements. Although the life of many construction elements is probably longer, lives in excess of 25 years produce small changes in the capital recovery factor for the interest rates used here. Pavement lives of 17 years have been assumed that correspond to average experience for well-constructed flexible pavements.[33]

For these facility lives total fixed and current line-haul trucking costs have been computed at an interest rate of 10%. They are shown by the unit cost curves plotted in Figure 3.6 for earth, gravel, and paved roads. In each case, both low- and high-cost curves are plotted so as to indicate the range of unit costs possible for each road type. The lower curves correspond to low construction costs (obtained by using low design speeds) and large trucks; the upper curves, to high construction costs and the use of smaller vehicles. The curves therefore are not strictly comparable, because, for equivalent volumes, higher unit cost curves represent some improvement in over-all operating speeds.

In measuring the output of alternative roads in Figure 3.6, their capacity to accommodate additional automobile traffic must also be taken into account. Such curves as those that are shown should not be compared with similar unit cost curves

[32] It should be emphasized, however, that the concept of facility life in the case of earth roads is useful only for accounting purposes. Earth roads are usually perpetuated through maintenance until such time as they are replaced by higher quality roads. The distinction between maintenance and actual capital replacement is therefore a difficult one to draw.

[33] Yoder, *op. cit.*, p. 537.

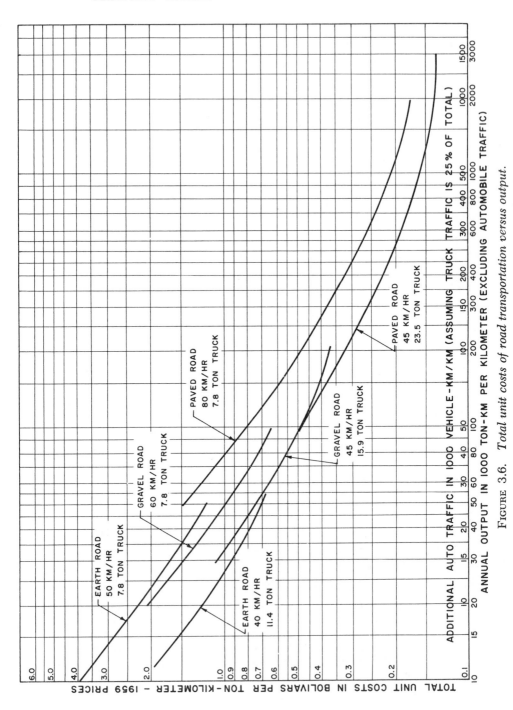

FIGURE 3.6. *Total unit costs of road transportation versus output.*

for other modes of transportation, for, in addition to the freight output, passenger transportation can also be produced. Non-freight output in terms of automobile-kilometers per kilometer has been estimated in Figure 3.6 by assuming truck traffic to be 25% of total traffic. Therefore for an average truck size of 15.9 tons operating with a 50% load factor, the estimated ratio of automobile to truck traffic is approximately 500 automobile-kilometers per 1000 ton-kilometers.

Some discontinuities are to be observed in Figure 3.6. The intersection of the unit cost curves for earth and gravel roads, for example, occurs at volumes beyond the capacity of the earth road. In fact, before this volume is reached, maintenance costs would be such as to cause the unit cost curve for earth roads to rise sharply. This produces a scalloped effect in the shape of the cost curves over the total range of volumes. In part, these discontinuities occur because only three types of fixed plant have been considered. Instead of proceeding directly from an earth to a gravel road, soil stabilization might be used to reduce maintenance costs and allow for slightly higher daily volumes. This would represent a different fixed plant, and a new unit cost curve could be plotted that would fall somewhere between the curves shown for earth and gravel roads. Similarly, a cost curve for penetration macadam roads would smooth out the discontinuity that occurs in moving directly from a gravel road to a well-paved one. As a result of this smoothing process, obtained by more gradual increases in the road fixed plant, the over-all unit cost curve covering the entire range of traffic volumes possible on two-lane roads would approach the envelope of the series of curves shown in Figure 3.6.[34]

In plotting total unit cost curves market prices have been used in aggregating the various cost elements. The various data presented in this chapter, however, allow the labor, local capital, and foreign exchange components of construction, main-

[34] For the general theory of cost curves and their envelopes, see Jacob Viner, "Cost Curves and Supply Curves," in *Readings in Price Theory*, George J. Stigler and Kenneth E. Boulding, eds. (Chicago: Richard D. Irwin, Inc., 1952), pp. 198–232.

Table 3.12. Labor, Local Capital, and Foreign Exchange Components of Total Road Transport Costs for Selected Traffic Volumes and Road Types at 10% Interest [1]

(in bolivars per ton-kilometer)

Annual Tonnage (Metric Tons)	Road Type	Low				High			
		Labor	Local Capital	Foreign Exchange	Total	Labor	Local Capital	Foreign Exchange	Total
50,000	Earth	0.303	0.216	0.148	0.667	0.405	0.349	0.231	0.985
	Gravel	0.303	0.267	0.175	0.745	0.399	0.372	0.234	1.005
	Paved	0.342	0.293	0.200	0.835	0.524	0.563	0.360	1.447
150,000	Gravel	0.178	0.140	0.093	0.411	0.234	0.178	0.108	0.520
	Paved	0.145	0.122	0.091	0.358	0.218	0.215	0.134	0.567
200,000	Gravel	0.162	0.122	0.082	0.366	0.220	0.155	0.092	0.467
	Paved	0.121	0.100	0.077	0.298	0.180	0.171	0.106	0.457
500,000	Paved	0.079	0.067	0.056	0.202	0.116	0.099	0.060	0.272
1,000,000	Paved	0.063	0.052	0.046	0.161	0.091	0.070	0.041	0.202
2,000,000	Paved	0.055	0.044	0.041	0.140	0.078	0.055	0.031	0.164

[1] All costs in 1959 bolivars.

tenance, and operating costs to be computed separately. The unit cost curves of Figure 3.6 could therefore be recalculated by applying accounting prices to the various components. Labor-capital substitutability could also be indicated. Although no attempt has been made here to redraw the unit cost curves on the basis of accounting prices, Table 3.12 does show the range of labor-capital substitutability possible for selected levels of transportation output.

REGIONAL TRANSPORTATION PLANNING: A CASE STUDY

The foregoing chapters attempt to answer the question of how one designs and operates a transport facility given the demand or level of service that the particular facility will be called upon to provide. In so doing, the problem of estimating transport demand is completely disregarded. Clearly, in any transportation planning problem, estimating demand is at least half the battle.

Estimating the traffic volume between two points on a particular transport facility usually involves two steps. First, the total volume of goods that will move between these two points by *all* modes of transport is estimated. Second, the distribution of this volume among *competing* modes of transport is determined. This second step is referred to as the *modal split problem.*

To the extent that transport technology affects transport charges, total demand may be affected by the choice of transport technology within a particular mode of transportation. This interdependence of demand and technology, moreover, is a two-way relationship since a change in demand (that is, level of transport output) may affect the selection of transport technology as pointed out in Chapter Two.

The choice of technology may also influence modal split. Modal split depends primarily upon transport charges in the case of goods movements, although other factors such as travel time, schedules, arrival time reliability, and susceptibility to pilferage and damage also affect a shipper's choice of travel mode. Where there are only slight differences in charges between competing modes, a change in technology within one mode may therefore affect modal split (assuming, of course, that charges are based on the cost of providing service).

Although the method of investigating technological choice described in Chapter Two deals only with road transportation, the same sort of analysis could presumably be carried for other modes of transportation. Modal split calculations could then be made, comparing each mode at its best technology.

Practically speaking, preliminary assignment of the flow of goods to alternative modes of transport is usually made without considering the question of technological choice.[1] Certain modal choices may be obvious, as in the case of transporting bulk commodities such as ore over large bodies of water. In other cases, differences in transport charges among competing modes may be so large that relatively small differences in charges brought about by changes in transport technology may not affect modal split. In addition, some estimate of investment requirements in the transport sector of the economy may often be needed for governmental programming before costs associated with alternative technologies can be investigated.[2]

Some of these practical difficulties are illustrated in the following case study that deals with transportation planning in a newly developing area of southeastern Venezuela known as the Guayana region. This case study is presented as an example of how estimates of transport investment were arrived at in an actual case of regional planning. No attempt is made to justify the lack of economic rigor or application of the methods expounded in Chapter Two, many of which only came to light as a result of this transportation planning exercise.

[1] When the volume or demand for each facility is determined, a choice of technology is then made. This selection, which is implicit in the engineer's choice of design standards, may not be the best choice in terms of the framework described previously.

[2] As Fromm points out, "The transport planner cannot be given special timing consideration for the submission of the transport sector plan document." Gary Fromm, "Design of the Transport Sector," in *Transport Investment and Economic Development*, Gary Fromm, ed. (Washington: The Brookings Institution, 1965), p. 97.

Background

To a very great extent the economy of Venezuela depends upon the production and export of petroleum products. Due in part to the current decline in the growth of petroleum exports, however, new resources upon which to build a broader economic base are being searched out and developed. Of these, one of the most important is the vast reserve of high grade iron ore concentrated in the Guayana region. Many of Venezuela's hopes for industrial diversification and economic development are presently focused around this region.

A map of the Guayana region is shown in Figure 4.1. In the Venezuelan context, this region includes the state of Bolívar and the federal territories of Amazonas and Delta Amacuro, comprising approximately 50% of the total area of Venezuela.[3] By contrast, only 3.45% of the total population (according to the 1961 census figures) lives within the boundaries of the Guayana region.

Due to the relatively small importance of the federal territories, the term "Guayana" is usually considered to be synonymous with the State of Bolívar, which contained 213,000 persons in 1961 (or 2.8% of the total Venezuelan population) and comprises an area of 238,000 square kilometers (or roughly one-fourth of the total country).[4]

In contrast to its low population density, the region enjoys an abundance of natural resources, principally high grade iron ore (up to 65% pure) and tremendous hydroelectric potential. The export of iron ore has been the principal economic activity of the region for the last 15 years. The major iron mining operation takes place at Cerro Bolívar, a mine owned by the Orinoco Mining Company (a subsidiary of the United States

[3] In a broader context, the term Guayana includes a large part of the territory bounded by the Orinoco and Amazon Rivers and also includes, therefore, parts of Brazil and the British, Dutch (Surinam), and French Guianas, as well as the Venezuelan Guayana.

[4] José Antonio Rangel, Lawrence Bridge, and Gordon A. Marker, *The Guayana Development Program*, draft prepared for the *Plan de la Nación, 1965–1968*, (Corporación Venezolana de Guayana, División de Planificación Sector Económico, March 1965), p. 2, File No. B-80.

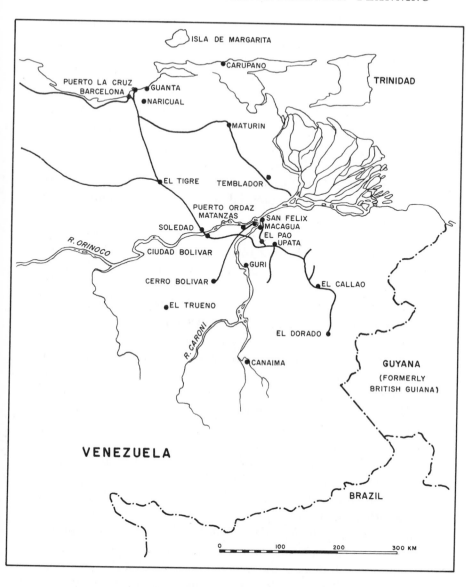

FIGURE 4.1. *Map of the Guayana region.*

79

Steel Corporation), which has produced as much as 20 million tons of ore annually. Ore is transported from the mine by a modern, highly efficient company railroad to Puerto Ordaz, a company town located at the confluence of the Orinoco and Caroní Rivers, where the ore is crushed and transshipped to ocean-going vessels. A smaller mine producing about 2 million tons annually is operated by Iron Mines Company of Venezuela (a subsidiary of Bethlehem Steel) at El Pao. This ore is also transported by private rail facilities to a company port at Palúa. In addition, as yet undeveloped, proven reserves of 1300 million tons and potential reserves of 4000 million tons are located at San Isidro and El Trueno.[5]

Since 1961, these iron mining activities have been supplemented by the opening of a government-owned steel mill at Matanzas (upstream from Puerto Ordaz), and the completion of a hydroelectric plant at Macagua. This hydroelectric project has a generating capacity of 370,000 kilowatts and represents the first stage in the electrification of the Caroní River, a project ultimately designed to generate 6 million kilowatts. Government-owned coal mines with proven reserves of 30 million tons have also been opened at Naricual on the northern coast, primarily as a source of supply for the steel mill. Activities of lesser importance which historically have been associated with the region include cattle breeding and diamond mining.

Principal population centers include Ciudad Bolívar, capital of the State of Bolívar, San Félix, a very old town located on the south bank of the Orinoco, Puerto Ordaz, and Upata. Good all-weather roads presently interconnect all of these towns. The road from Puerto Ordaz along the south bank of the Orinoco to Ciudad Bolívar which then continues to El Tigre from the north bank is the major link to the rest of Venezuela. The World Bank is presently sponsoring construction of a bridge across the Orinoco River at this point to replace the existing ferry service. A bridge over the Caroní River connecting Puerto Ordaz and San Félix was completed in 1964.

In 1960, a development agency known as the Corporación

[5] Rangel, *op. cit.*, p. 3.

Venezolana de Guayana (Guayana Development Corporation) was established by the Venezuelan government in order to take advantage of the concentration and complementarity of mineral and energy resources found in the region.[6] Specifically, the governmental decree creating the CVG assigned to it the following objectives:[7]

1. Study Guayana's resources not only in the zone of development but also outside its boundaries whenever their nature so required.

2. Study, develop, and organize harnessing the hydroelectric potential of the Caroní River.

3. Program the integral development of the region according to norms and within the scope of a national plan.

4. Promote the industrial development of the region in the public as well as the private sector.

5. Coordinate activities in the economic and social field carried out in the region by the different government agencies.

6. Contribute to the organization, programming, development, and operation of those public agencies required for the development of the zone.

7. Carry out, by decision of the national executive, any other task that may have reference to operations outside the boundaries of the zone, whenever any close relationships exist with those being carried out in it.

This autonomous government authority was charged with the responsibility for programming the integrated economic development of southeastern Venezuela. As such, it assumed duties formerly performed by the Venezuelan Institute of Iron and Steel, the Commission for the Electrification of the Caroní, and undertook administration of the government coal mines at Naricual. The establishment of such an agency represented one of the first attempts to organize a planning operation for a completely integrated industrial complex on a region-wide basis. Under its direction plans for the industrial development

[6] Further undeveloped resources include proven reserves of 2,200 million barrels of oil and 320 thousand million cubic meters of natural gas in eastern part of the region.

[7] Rangel, *op. cit.*, pp. 8–9.

of the Guayana region have been under preparation for the past several years. Briefly, the procedure followed in the planning process as described in the *Guayana Development Program* can be outlined as follows:[8]

1. Select a preliminary list of resource-oriented industries and industrial complexes.

2. Elaborate the initial list according to the following criteria: national and world demand, minimum economic scale, complementarity, competitive costs, transportation, existence of a hydroelectric plant and steel mill, and relation to national plans and goals.

3. Establish long-term output goals for the selected industries, starting from national and export demand projections. These output goals would in turn serve as a basis for determining value of output and value added, required investment, required labor force and its composition, consumption of electricity, and space requirements.

4. Estimate employment and output for complementary manufacturing activities and services, starting from basic employment.

5. Make population projections based on total employment, which in turn supply the preliminary basic information for urban designers and planners, and also for estimated infrastructure requirements.

6. Draw up projections for regional demand and supply (paying particular attention to income variations) and develop a preliminary table of demand (consumption, investment, and exports), and of supply (output and imports) so as to establish the likely external requirements and potential outflows.

7. Analyze financing for the program, estimating availability of national and international resources, both public and private.

8. Refine parameters according to the conclusions of studies, experience, and new circumstances, and staging of investments. This step requires translating the long-term program into medium- and short-term programs and into specific projects.

9. Promote and coordinate the financing operation of the program.

10. Maintain control, evaluation, and adjustment of the program.

The most important activities now in the planning stage include the creation of a heavy industrial complex centered around the existing steel mill, a joint venture on the part of the

[8] Rangel, *op. cit.*, p. 13.

development corporation and a private corporation to construct an aluminum plant in the same area, further electrification of the Caroní through the construction of a large dam at Guri (65 kilometers upstream from Macagua), and the opening of government iron mines at San Isidro. In addition, plans also exist for development of an iron ore reduction process, for the construction of a manganese ore reduction plant, and for the creation of small-scale wood products and construction materials industries. Selected production targets and population estimates based on these targets are summarized in Table 4.1.

Table 4.1. Selected Long-Term Targets
Guayana Region, 1965, 1968, 1975

Item	Units	1965	1968	1975
I Totals				
1. Population	thousands of persons	95	152	413
2. Employment	thousands of persons	29	50	133
3. Value of Production	millions of bolivars	1,490	2,882	13,467
4. Value Added	millions of bolivars	957	1,750	8,073
5. Fixed Investment	millions of bolivars	665	1,002	2,214
6. Construction	millions of bolivars	401	530	1,115
II Per Capita				
1. Value of Production	millions of bolivars	15.7	19.0	32.6
2. Value Added	thousands of bolivars	10.1	11.5	19.5
3. Fixed Investment	thousands of bolivars	7.0	6.6	5.4

Source: José Antonio Rangel, Lawrence Bridge, Gordon A. Marker, *The Guayana Development Program*, draft prepared for the *Plan de la Nación, 1965–1968*, (Corporación Venezolana de Guayana, División de Planificación Sector Económico, March 1965), p. 6, File No. B-80.

One of the major characteristics of the regional development plan is the concentration of industrial activities at the confluence of the Orinoco and Caroní Rivers within the area bounded by the steel mill on the West and San Félix on the East. Because of interindustry relationships and because the Orinoco affords deep water shipping for both domestic and world markets, many of the new industries are being planned in close proximity to one another within this area. Due to the magnitude of the estimated employment in these new industries, the development agency is also involved in planning a new city named Santo Tomé de Guayana (Ciudad Guayana), encompassing what are now the towns of Puerto Ordaz and San Félix. Estimates place the population of this new city at approximately 600,000 by 1980; the 1963 urban population was about 55,000.

Planning an urban area to accommodate the anticipated urban population presents problems of equal if not greater proportions than problems of implementing the industrial program itself. On one hand, the magnitude of the investment in social overhead needed to keep pace with the rapid growth of population must be kept low enough so as not to detract from the over-all profitability of investing in the region. On the other hand, because climatological factors and amenities are inferior to those of the more populous centers of the country such as Caracas, there is a need to make living in the area sufficiently pleasant to attract the labor and managerial skills necessary for the implementation of the development plan.

The investment in social overhead is estimated to be sizable. In the field of housing, for example, estimated needs are for 55,000 new units over the next twelve years. During the next three years alone, housing investment must be sufficient to provide at least 17,000 new units. A large part of this investment, moreover, will come from government sources because Venezuelan labor legislation requires the employer (in this case the government-owned steel plant) to pay the cost of portal-to-portal transportation including wages while in transit. As a result, the usual incentive for an employee to seek a home close to his work is removed, and home-to-work travel distances tend to be maximized. The situation is further complicated because the steel plant is located at a considerable distance from existing centers of population and available housing. Until recently, many workers were commuting daily from Ciudad Bolívar, some 80 kilometers away, and even now the average journey to work is from 15 to 20 kilometers. The alternative to paying the costs of transportation associated with these long work trips is to provide housing near the centers of employment.

Aside from social overhead investment in the new city itself, investments will be required to reduce the costs of transportation between the region and the rest of the country. At the present time, the Guayana is a food-deficit area and with the anticipated growth in population the cost of transporting foods and other consumer goods to the region will become an increasingly important factor. The extensive distances[9] separating the region from areas where consumer goods are produced tend to raise costs of living; high living costs are eventually reflected in higher costs of production. Thus transport costs, through their effect on costs of production and distribution, seriously influence the competitive advantage of the Guayana region relative to other regions of the country.

However, the resources of the region have been proved, and the major transport investments needed to initiate development have already been made.[10] Railroads and deepwater shipping facilities needed for the extraction and export of iron ore now exist. The region is linked to the rest of Venezuela by first-class roads and within the region itself more than adequate all-weather roads provide access to practically any point where transport demand exists. The major transportation planning problems of the region therefore relate less to questions of *where* to provide new transport facilities than to determining what increases in the capacity of existing routes will be consistent with over-all development goals.

The Demand for Transportation

Transportation is similar to any other good offered in the market inasmuch as more of it will be demanded as its price

[9] Caracas is 750 kilometers from the proposed new city, while food-producing areas west of Valencia are approximately 890 kilometers away.

[10] There has been a great deal of speculation about mineral riches in large areas of the Guayana region that still remain unexplored. Should such riches eventually be proved, new transport routes will be required, routes that might well be characterized by the dramatic development effects referred to in Chapter One.

is reduced. However, the demand for transportation is a derived demand, and its price sensitivity rests largely upon the magnitude of transportation costs relative to the total value of the commodity moved. Ideally, the over-all demand for transportation could be projected by estimating the demand (function) for each commodity, the respective supply (function), and the unit costs associated with transporting the commodity to its market. The equilibrium output obtained by equating supply (including transportation costs) and demand could then be determined for each commodity produced in the region, and summed to give the total demand for freight transportation at a given point in time.

Transport costs also affect demand in a more indirect manner. For example, the costs of transporting foods and other consumer goods to the Guayana region lead to high costs of living and correspondingly high wage rates. All other things being equal, these higher wages in turn lead to higher costs of production than might be found in other areas of the country. Thus, even though for many goods the cost of transporting them may not loom large in terms of their total value, transport costs might be reflected indirectly in higher production costs and subsequent reduction in demand.

Partly because of timing considerations and partly for lack of the relevant demand-function data, the demand for final goods that could be produced competitively in the Guayana region was determined on the basis of historical trends, notably past experience with the effects of rising per capita income on the consumption of various goods and services. These estimates of domestic demand were coupled with predictions of the demand for exports, based on an analysis of future Latin American and world markets.[11] On the basis of these demand

[11] See the following mimeographed reports of the Corporación Venezolana de Guayana, Joint Center-Guayana Project, Caracas: Alexander Ganz, *Preliminary Perspectives on the Role of the Guayana Region in the Economic Development of Venezuela*, File B-6, 26 March 1962; Alexander Ganz, *World Demand for Present and Potential Guayana Region Minerals, Metals, Machinery and Chemical Fertilizer Products; and Rest-of-Venezuela Demand for Guayana Region Metals and Machinery Products 1960–61, 1961–65–70–80–2000*, File B-14, 7 May 1962; and Leonard Fischman, *Notes on the Domestic and Export Markets for Certain Selected Materials*, File D-14, 16 June 1962.

estimates, a list of potential industrial projects for the Guayana region was drawn up taking into account the resource endowments that would give this region particular competitive advantage. These resources include the availability of very high grade iron ore, relatively cheap hydroelectric potential, access to nearby deposits of natural gas and petroleum, and the existence of deepwater shipping facilities.

An analysis of potential industrial activities on the basis of locational factors (access to both supplies and markets), costs of production, minimum economic scale, complementary nature of activities, and other factors affecting the competitive position of the Guayana region with respect to alternative locations in the country led to the development of targets for the production of goods and services for various years. These targets were then translated into estimates of employment and income levels that were subsequently used as the basis for estimates of the future population of the region and of the planned center of industrial activity in the new city of Santo Tomé de Guayana (Ciudad Guayana).[12]

The data obtained from this procedure that are relevant for purposes of transportation planning are summarized in Tables 4.2 and 4.3, where industrial production targets and population predictions are shown, respectively.

Given these estimates of production and population, the total demand for transportation can be separated into the following categories:

a. Transportation of the primary input materials necessary for production.

b. Transportation of final goods produced to other locations in the region, country, and the world.

c. Transportation of agricultural products and of consumer goods not produced locally that are necessary to sustain populations of the indicated magnitudes.

d. Passenger transportation.

[12] See Alexander Ganz, *Regional Planning as a Key to the Present Stage of Economic Development of Latin America; The Case of the Guayana Region, a Frontier Region.* Paper presented at the First Latin American Regional Science Congress, Caracas, November 12–14, 1962, pp. 4–5.

Table 4.2. Industrial Production Targets for
Ciudad Guayana

Industry	Production in 1000 Metric Tons			
	1966	1970	1975	1980
Furnace and Rolling Mill Products	990	1,970	3,720	6,380
Reduced Iron Ore	150	5,000	10,000	15,000
Iron Ore for Export	20,000	21,200	25,000	25,000
Aluminum	50	100	200	500
Manganese Metal	—	20	30	80
Magnesium	—	—	—	20
Machinery and Equipment	—	80	155	200
Chemicals	120	120	338	695
Construction Materials	—	310	490	750
Forest Products	—	—	115	220
Total	21,310	28,800	40,048	48,845

Source: George Perazich, *Preliminary Program of Potential Industrial Development Projects for the Guayana Region,* (Caracas: Corporación Venezolana de Guayana, Joint Center-Guayana Project, 26 March 1962), pp. 17–23 and Economic Planning Staff, Corporación Venezolana de Guayana, Joint Center-Guayana Project.

Table 4.3. Population Prediction for Bolívar State

	Population in 1000's				
	1961	1966[1]	1970	1975[1]	1980
Santo Tomé de Guayana	42	128	240	440	640
Ciudad Bolívar	64	84	110	140	170
Other Urban Areas with more than 2,500	27	31	37	43	50
Rural	80	82	85	87	88
Total	213	325	472	710	948

[1] Based on linear interpolation.

Source: Economic Planning Staff, Corporación Venezolana de Guayana, Joint Center-Guayana Project.

Passenger transportation is not considered here because of its relatively minor importance in terms of new transportation facilities. As previously noted, good road connections to the rest of Venezuela already exist. Moreover, owing to the extensive distances separating the region from major urban centers in the rest of the country, air transportation will probably remain the most important means of intercity passenger transportation. Highway capacity increases will thus undoubtedly stem from increases in freight using this mode. For other modes, such as railroads and shipping, of course, passenger transportation does not represent an important consideration.

Demand estimates for items *a*, *b*, and *c* are treated in detail in Appendix B (p. 131). On the basis of calculations shown in the appendix, commodity flow estimates have been prepared and summarized in Table 4.4. Flow diagrams for the year 1975 are shown in Figures 4.2 and 4.3. Such diagrams are useful in indicating those origins and destinations which can be grouped along principal transportation routes. They also clearly point out the directionality or imbalance of incoming and outgoing flows for the region.

The data from which Table 4.3 was developed indicate the dominance of steel as an outgoing commodity flow when shipments of minerals are excluded. Moreover, since estimates of regional imports have been derived directly from estimates of production, the flow of furnace and rolling mill products can be said to dominate the entire pattern of commodity flows to and from the region. Steel production levels also determine the volumes of coal and limestone required from the Puerto La Cruz area. The demand for freight transportation is seen to be highly sensitive to changes in the demand for furnace and rolling mill products.

The dependency of total transportation demand on steel production levels suggests the use of steel output as a check in making estimates of future transportation requirements. Periodic checks of development progress could be made by comparing the level of steel production at any future time with the level originally predicted and then making appropriate adjustments to the regional transportation plan.

Table 4.4. Summary of Total Estimated Commodity Flows To and From Ciudad Guayana

Origin or Destination	Annual Commodity Flows in 1000 Metric Tons							
	1966		1970		1975		1980	
	In	Out	In	Out	In	Out	In	Out
Iron ore								
Cerro Bolívar	14,000	—	14,000	—	14,000	—	14,000	—
El Pao	6,000	—	6,000	—	6,000	—	6,000	—
San Isidro	2,100	—	12,900	—	28,000	—	31,000	—
Export		20,300		24,600		33,000		37,800
Total	22,100	20,300	32,900	24,600	48,000	33,000	51,000	37,800
Other								
Delta Amacuro	200	—	400	—	800	—	2,000	—
East Guayana	—	—	—	—	290	—	550	—
Guacuripa	320	—	720	—	1,340	—	2,390	—
Apure	4	—	6	—	11	—	17	—
Barinas	—	19	—	45	—	101	—	185
Barquisimeto	—	4	—	10	—	21	—	39
Caracas	65	131	104	319	172	698	246	1,270
Coro	140	—	140	—	350	—	700	—
El Tigre	—	24	—	58	—	124	—	227
Guárico	5	—	8	—	14	—	22	—
Maracaibo	12	77	25	192	47	416	79	755

Maracay	29	23	42	55	68	120	89	219
Margarita	—	—	—	—	100	—	100	—
Maturín	6	27	10	64	19	139	30	253
Naricual	420	—	840	—	1,580	—	2,720	—
Pertigalete	281	—	631	—	1,130	—	2,080	—
Puerto Cabello	14	2	21	5	34	10	44	19
Puerto La Cruz	27	8	45	23	109	50	194	88
Valencia	51	113	83	298	138	622	201	1,120
West of Valencia	25	—	40	—	68	—	103	—
Valera	—	16	—	38	—	86	—	158
Export	549	640	1,095	1,020	2,074	1,800	3,588	3,040
Total (excluding iron ore)	2,148	1,084	4,210	2,127	8,344	4,187	15,150	7,373

91

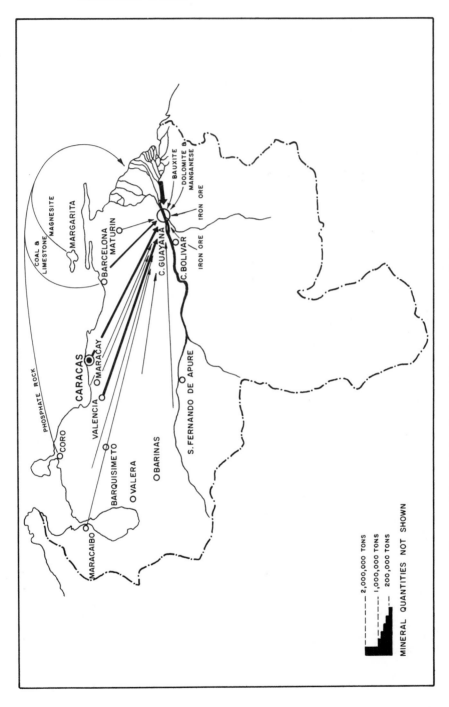

FIGURE 4.2. *Origin of commodity flows entering Bolivar State in 1975.*

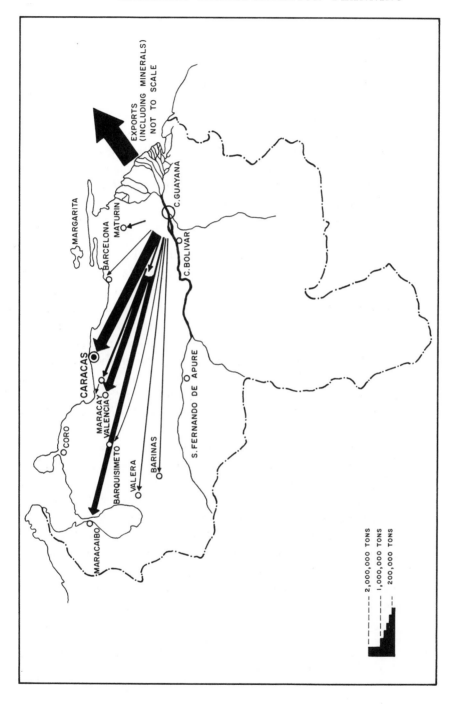

FIGURE 4.3. *Destination of commodity flows originating in Bolivar State in 1975.*

There is, of course, some uncertainty involved in making these commodity flow estimates, stemming in part from national or world conditions that are outside the control of regional planners.[13] Uncertainty stemming from estimates of Venezuelan population growth and from estimates of the growth rate of the Venezuelan economy also affect both the type and level of production achieved in the Guayana region.

The uncertainty involved in the production targets that have been discussed is of two types. The first concerns whether or not *all* the planned industrial activities will in fact materialize, that is, whether there will be any demand whatsoever for the products of certain industries and, if so, when. The second type of uncertainty pertains to the level of demand which materializes for industries that eventually go into production.

The proposed iron ore reduction plant is an example of the first type of uncertainty. The economics of such an iron ore reduction plant rests on the feasibility of using a gas reduction process that could take advantage of natural gas available from nearby sources. The opening of the iron ore reduction plant thus depends on the technical feasibility of the natural gas process aside from any consideration of the market for such ore. In the event that this process should not prove feasible, it would be safe to assume that no reduced iron ore would be produced for export.

In a similar manner (although the quantities involved are much smaller) manganese ore processing depends upon finding commercial deposits of manganese ore in the region. (The quality and extent of the manganese known to exist there have not yet been proved.) If such deposits are not discovered, the region is likely to become an importer of manganese metal rather than an exporter. Similarly, in the case of bauxite necessary for the production of aluminum, detailed investigation of the available reserves will determine whether or not the region becomes an importer of the ore.

[13] In a study of economic growth in Venezuela, for example, Friedmann states that "ultimately, Venezuela's destiny will not be determined by an act of the will . . . but by exogenous events . . ." John Friedmann, *Economic Growth and Urban Structure in Venezuela; Towards a Dynamic Theory of Spatial Organization* (Caracas: Corporación Venezolana de Guayana, Joint Center-Guayana Project, 12 November 1962), p. 4 (mimeographed).

The second type of uncertainty relates to the level of production in those industries for which some demand is eventually generated. For many of the industries under consideration, a certain minimum level of demand is almost guaranteed, particularly if government controls are introduced. For example, a large part of the anticipated production of the Guayana industrial complex is planned to replace basic commodities presently being imported. Moreover, for many of these commodities the Guayana region will be the only source of domestic production for some time to come (as, for example, structural steel shapes, reinforcing bars, rails, and sheet metal). Therefore a government decision to close the door on further imports of these products would immediately create a demand for domestic producers, although the extent of this demand as well as the demand for exports still depends upon prices, quality, and national population and economic growth rates. Precedent has already been set for this sort of action in a very well-defined program for reducing imports of automobiles.[14]

The major effects of these uncertainties relate to the capacity and quality of the transport network that must be provided (and hence to the investment requirements of the transport sector). In addition, as shown in the section that follows, the question of what modes of transportation ought to be provided hinges to a very great extent on the levels of transport demand that materialize. In view of these uncertainties, it should be emphasized that the estimates of transport demand summarized here represent estimates of what the transportation needs of the region would be *if production were to achieve* the level projected by the economic planning staff, as shown in Table 4.1. Implicit in these production estimates is the assumption that sufficient transport capacity would be available, although, explicitly, no allowance was made for the interaction between transport capacity and the demand for the goods that could be produced in the region.

---

[14] See Oficina Central de Coordinación y Planificación, *Elementos Para Una Política de Desarrollo de la Industria Automotríz en Venezuela,* Report to the Comisión Económica del Consejo de Ministros (Caracas, 1962).

Alternative Transport Plans

Commodity flow estimates for the Guayana Region indicate the need for both water and overland transportation systems. The location of major urban areas and centers of production in Venezuela is such that water transportation should represent a much more important component of the transportation system than it does. Water transportation is particularly suited to the Guayana industrial complex, for water routes are available to practically all the major urban and industrial areas along the northern coast of Venezuela. At the present time, however, domestic water transportation is discouraged by inefficient port administration, excessive port handling charges, and high shipping costs for Venezuelan flag vessels. Despite these poor conditions, shipping still enjoys a competitive advantage for the transportation of certain commodities. Moreover, in view of the bulk nature of commodity flows anticipated to originate from this region, the relative importance of shipping as a mode of transportation for the Guayana region can be expected to increase in the future.

Within overland transportation systems the question of road versus rail becomes an important consideration. Railroads are currently a controversial issue in Venezuela. Although at one time railroad lines were to be found throughout the country, many of these were abandoned as highways were improved and trucking became more competitive. The competitive disadvantage of railroad transportation was in no small part due to the decentralized nature of its organization, composed as it was of separate lines operating on different gauge track. Today, railroading in Venezuela is limited to four separate lines (excluding the privately owned lines of the Orinoco Mining Company and the Iron Mines Company of Venezuela in the Guayana region). The Gran Ferrocarril de Tachira (105 kilometers from La Fria to Encontrados south of Lake Maracaibo) and the Gran Ferrocarril de Venezuela (177 kilometers from Caracas to Valencia) are both old, narrow-gauge lines that have suffered steadily increasing operating losses and decreasing traffic volumes. The former will undoubtedly be abandoned following completion of the La Fria–Machiques highway now being planned.[15] The two remaining lines are the recently constructed 173-kilometer Gran Ferrocarril Puerto Cabello running between Puerto Cabello and Barquisimeto and the new 27-kilometer railroad running from coal mines at Naricual to the northern port of Guanta.

Despite the present state of railroad development in the country, pressures do exist for further railroad construction. A national commission has strongly urged the construction of an extensive system of railroads running from east to west across the nation with branches to San Cristóbal and San Félix in the south.[16] Although attempts have been made to demonstrate the economic viability of such a system, the basic arguments really rest on the belief that any nation undergoing industrialization should equip itself with an adequate system of railroads. Separate proposals have also been made for the construction of a railroad between Guanta and Matanzas for the purpose of transporting coal and limestone to the steel mill.[17]

Contrary to these proposals, a World Bank mission to Venezuela strongly recommended that no further railroad construction be undertaken anywhere in Venezuela. The mission argued that railroad construction would constitute an unnecessary duplication of transport facilities, particularly in view of the high costs of construction and low revenues experienced on the recently constructed Gran Ferrocarril Puerto Cabello.[18]

In view of this situation, at least two alternative overland transport schemes might reasonably be considered for the

[15] This old and very picturesque railroad carries Venezuelan and Colombian coffee (which arrives by way of a rail connection from Cucuta) to Encontrados where it is transshipped to river barges and then carried to Maracaibo for export. The new highway will thus eliminate at least two transshipments and provide service which is much more rapid.

[16] *Informe Económico Sobre un Plan Ferroviario Nacional* (Caracas: Comisión Económica Ferroviaria Nacional, 1960).

[17] See, for example, Pascual A. Abramián, *La Siderúrgica Nacional y el Problema de Los Transportes de Las Materias Primas y Acabados* (Caracas: Comisión Económica Ferroviaria Nacional, 28 December 1959), mimeographed.

[18] International Bank for Reconstruction and Development, *The Economic Development of Venezuela* (Baltimore: The Johns Hopkins Press, 1961), pp. 452–456.

Guayana region. First, a highway-dominant plan involving no further railroad construction might be considered—certainly a reasonable proposal in view of past experience and in view of the World Bank report. Second, a plan including construction of the Guanta-Matanzas line might be considered. The economic feasibility of such a line may look better now than when the industrial growth perspectives of the Guayana region were somewhat more limited.

In order to evaluate these alternative schemes, some estimate of the manner in which cargo will be distributed among alternative modes of transportation must be made. Assigning traffic to alternative modes of transport requires some background of information about the relative cost characteristics of those modes. In Appendices C and D (pp. 146 and 149), therefore, the relevant cost data for shipping and railroad transportation under Venezuelan conditions are considered briefly. The available information on these modes of transport is very limited, and for this reason estimates of representative costs for rail and water transportation have been used. These estimates are based largely on data that could be gleaned from reports to various government agencies and on some data provided by private operators. The range of values obtained from these sources was often extremely large. In cases where no Venezuelan data could be obtained, comparative data from other countries provided the basis for the cost estimates used. Road transportation costs, on the other hand, are based on data developed in Chapter Three.

Despite the uncertainties involved in these estimates of shipping and railroad costs, they are used for lack of better data to make preliminary interregional commodity flow assignments to alternative transport modes under both the highway-dominant and railroad-dominant transport plans.

Highway-Dominant Plan

Under this plan it is assumed that all commodity flows to and from the region would be handled by truck, ship, and truck-ship combinations of transportation. With the exception of a spur line from the existing Orinoco Mining Company railroad to the government iron mines at San Isidro, it is further assumed that no additional railroads would be constructed within the region. Under these circumstances and in view of the types of commodities to be moved, the manner in which commodity movements are distributed between truck and ship modes of transport depends to a great extent on the relative costs of shipping by each mode and any government policy of subsidization. The need for the latter will depend upon any discrepancies that exist between relative freight rates for the two modes and their relative real costs to the economy.

Preliminary assignment of commodity flows to the alternative modes of transport can be made by determining the relative cost advantage of ship and truck for the major origins and destinations of goods leaving and entering the region. For certain commodities there is little choice in the mode of transportation to be used. Magnesite from the island of Margarita, for example, must obviously be transported by ship. Similarly, phosphate rock from the island of Coro, limestone from Pertigalete, and coal from Guanta will also move by ship since in each case bulk commodities are involved for which both terminal costs and line-haul costs by ship are likely to be considerably less than by truck. On the other hand, goods moving to El Tigre and Maturín will almost certainly go by truck, since moving them by ship via Puerto La Cruz would result in no saving in over-all trucking distances.

Estimates of the relative costs of transporting finished steel products by truck and by ship from Matanzas to various destinations in the country are shown in Table 4.5. Note that trucking costs include only fully distributed operating costs (both fixed and variable) without any allowance for road construction or maintenance costs. For those destinations that are not ports, shipping costs have been estimated to the nearest port and allowances made for transporting goods by truck for the remaining distance. The basis for these cost calculations is explained in Appendix E (p. 152).

In allocating shipping costs to general cargo, only incremental costs and not fully distributed average costs were considered. In other words, if a ship that brings limestone from Guanta is also used to carry structural steel, or other forms of

Table 4.5. A Comparison of Shipping and Trucking Costs for General Cargo Originating in Ciudad Guayana[1]

Destination	Nearest Port	Ship-Truck Combination[3]				Truck Only[3]			Difference in Bs/Ton
		Shipping Costs in Bs/Ton	Remaining Road Distance in Km	Trucking Costs in Bs/Ton[2]	Total Costs in Bs/Ton	Road Distance in Bs/Ton	Total Costs[2] in Bs/Ton		
Caracas	La Guaira	59.4	20	9.6	69.0	745	96.5		27.5
Maracay	Puerto Cabello	61.6	107	20.0	81.6	754	98.0		16.4
Valencia	Puerto Cabello	61.6	57	14.0	75.6	796	102.7		27.1
Puerto Cabello	Puerto Cabello	61.6	—	7.2	68.8	853	109.7		40.9
Barquisimeto	Puerto Cabello	61.6	173	28.0	89.6	984	125.2		35.6
Barinas	Puerto Cabello	61.6	417	57.2	118.8	1156	146.7		27.9
Valera	Maracaibo	70.5	216	33.1	103.6	1229	154.7		51.1
Maracaibo	Maracaibo	70.5	—	7.2	77.7	1304	164.2		86.5

[1] 1959 prices.
[2] Includes Bs 7.2/ton for loading and unloading and line-haul costs of Bs 0.12/ton-km.
[3] Trucking costs do not include road construction or maintenance costs.

general cargo including containers, to La Guaira, the only costs charged against the general cargo are those over and above the costs that would have been incurred had the ship returned directly to Guanta. These incremental costs include:

1. Terminal charges for loading the general cargo in Matanzas and unloading it in La Guaira.

2. Daily operating charges for the additional time spent in port (both Matanzas and La Guaira).

3. Daily operating charges for the difference in trip time between returning directly to Guanta and returning via La Guaira.

Table 4.5 shows that despite very high terminal costs for general cargo, ship and ship-truck combinations of transport result in lower costs of transport than highway transportation alone for all destinations shown. For many of the finished steel products, lead time in ordering will be sufficient to compensate for the additional travel time associated with transport by ship. This is particularly true in the case of such commodities as the seamless steel pipe and structural steel that represent a large proportion of total steel production.[19]

The cost differentials of Table 4.5 might be increased substantially through future improvements in port administration and procedures for handling domestic cargo. (The latter are now similar to procedures used in handling cargo from foreign ports.)[20] In fact, much lower handling charges than have been estimated here have been incurred in the past.[21] Moreover, even

---

[19] In other words, customers for steel pipe will usually know their requirements far enough in advance to permit shipments to be made by boat. Anticipating the delays of ship transportation, however, such customers will maintain larger supplies on hand, thereby incurring higher inventory costs. See, for example, John R. Meyer et al., *The Economics of Competition in the Transportation Industries* (Cambridge, Mass.: Harvard University Press, 1959), Appendix D, pp. 348–53.

[20] International Bank, *op. cit.*, pp. 271–272.

[21] Average terminal costs in La Guaira, for example, rose from Bs 18.9 per ton in 1957 to Bs 49.9 per ton in 1959. *Informe de la Comisión Para el Estudio del Funcionamiento de los Puertos de Venezuela* (Caracas: Colegio de Ingenieros de Venezuela, 7 April, 1960), p. 11 (mimeographed). Sánchez Naranjo, *op. cit.*, p. 109, estimates unloading costs of Bs 16 to 20 per ton and loading costs of Bs 6 per ton.

if terminal charges should maintain their present levels, the large labor component of such charges makes the cost differentials in terms of real costs larger than those indicated in Table 4.5.

Despite the cost advantage of water transportation, there will undoubtedly be a substantial demand for truck transportation. For many high-value commodities, savings in transport costs associated with using water transportation may not be significant in terms of the total value of the goods involved. For others, shipments might be too small to permit economical handling by ship. In addition, road transportation will be the only available mode of transport for such destinations as Maturín and El Tigre and must be considered, therefore, even if all goods destined to the locations shown in Table 4.5 were to move by water.

In determining the highway needs of the region, only the incremental costs incurred over and above those needed to provide minimum road transport facilities for the region are of interest. For the major routes now leading to the region (the El Tigre–Soledad road including the bridge now under construction over the Orinoco at Ciudad Bolívar and the Templador–Los Barrancos road), this incremental cost includes the cost of improving road surfaces to carry the heavier truck volumes that are anticipated. The costs of increasing the capacity of these routes through widening or through the construction of additional bridges across the Orinoco River must also be included in evaluating the costs of the road transportation plan.

Capacity requirements and their associated costs depend upon estimated traffic volumes for future years. In Table 4.6, estimates of the average daily truck traffic that would be required to transport *all* commodity flows (excluding bulk commodities from Coro, Guanta, and Isla de Margarita) for the indicated years have been summarized. Truck volumes include those necessary to accommodate both outgoing production and incoming consumer goods and are based on the truck utilization factors developed previously in Chapter 3.

The implications of these truck volumes for highway capacity requirements are also summarized in Table 4.6 in terms of

Table 4.6. Estimated Average Daily Truck Traffic Between Ciudad Guayana and Selected Points Showing Capacity Requirements Assuming All Domestic Steel Products Are Transported by Truck

Truck Traffic[1] Between Ciudad Guayana and	1966		1970		1975		1980	
	1000 Tons	Daily Two-Way Trucks	1000 Tons	Daily Two-Way Trucks	1000 Tons	Daily Two-Way Trucks	1000 Tons	Daily Two-Way Trucks
Maturín	33	14	74	31	158	66	283	119
El Tigre	24	10	58	24	124	52	227	95
Guarico	5	2	8	3	14	6	22	9
Puerto La Cruz	35	15	68	29	159	67	282	118
Caracas	196	82	423	178	870	365	1517	637
Maracay	52	22	97	41	188	79	308	129
Valencia	164	69	381	160	760	319	1326	557
West of Valencia	25	10	40	17	68	29	103	43
Puerto Cabello	16	7	26	11	44	18	63	26
Barquisimeto	4	2	10	4	21	9	39	16
Valera	16	7	38	16	86	36	158	66
Barinas	19	8	45	19	101	42	185	78
Apure	4	2	6	3	11	5	17	7
Maracaibo	89	37	217	91	463	194	834	350
Total	682	287	1491	627	3067	1287	5364	2250
Required two-lane roads								
at 90 trucks/hr		1		1		2		3
at 140 trucks/hr		1		1		2		2

[1] Average truck size of 15.9 tons with 50% load factor.

103

the total number of two-lane roads leading to the region that would be required. Capacity requirements must also include an allowance for automobile traffic. It was assumed first that truck traffic would account for 25% of total daily traffic (as compared to 35% presently crossing the Orinoco River)[22] and that 12% of this truck traffic would be concentrated in the peak hour. Assuming that 16% of daily automobile traffic is also concentrated in the peak hour, truck traffic would then account for 20% of the total peak hour volume. In Table 4.6, the low capacity of 90 trucks per hour for each two-lane road corresponds to rolling terrain with poor passing opportunities; the higher figure is estimated for flat terrain with adequate passing-sight distances over the entire length.[23] The low estimate is thus very conservative since the present regional road from El Tigre to Soledad has practically no horizontal curvature and traverses terrain where gradients are negligible. From Ciudad Bolívar to Ciudad Guayana passing opportunities are reduced, but rates of rise and fall remain very low.

On the basis of these calculations, it appears that three, and possibly two, two-lane roads will be adequate to handle all truck traffic for 1980. Moreover, if average truck sizes increase over future years, average daily truck traffic would be less than that shown in Table 4.6. Thus, at most, the existing two-lane road to El Tigre would require widening to four lanes, and a second bridge across the Orinoco River connecting Ciudad Guayana to the Templador–Los Barrancos road would be required. With the second bridge, however, widening the road to El Tigre might well be unnecessary since much of the automobile traffic bound for Caracas and the northwest would be diverted to the Los Barrancos–Templador route. For at least the next 10 years, however, the existing two-lane road to the rest of the country would be adequate, even if it were assumed

[22] It is possible, of course, that automobile traffic may grow at a faster rate than truck traffic. In view of the extensive distances separating Ciudad Guayana from major cities, however, the growth of pleasure highway traffic would probably be less than that of commercial traffic, particularly since the proportion of truck oriented industries in the region is estimated to increase.

[23] These figures were derived from Comisión de Normas, *Normas Para el Proyecto de Carreteras* (Caracas: Ministerio de Obras Públicas, 1962), p. 40.

that all commodities produced for domestic use are transported by truck.

The pattern of commodity movements that eventually evolves will undoubtedly represent some combination of ship and truck transportation. The shipping *costs* that have been developed differ widely from the shipping *rates* currently quoted by Venezuelan shipping companies.[24] These companies presently employ much smaller ships than those upon which the above cost estimates have been based. Substantial potential for water transportation would probably have to be demonstrated before shipping companies would incur the initial expenditures for larger vessels. High utilization would also have to be guaranteed before lower rates could be offered to attract the necessary traffic.

Nevertheless, due to the large differential between trucking costs and costs of water transportation, almost all finished steel products destined to Maracaibo might reasonably be assumed to be transported by ship. It might further be assumed that at least 50% of finished steel products (excluding machinery and equipment) destined for the Caracas-Maracay-Valencia industrial belt would move by ship. A large share of these estimated commodity flows includes steel shapes for construction industries, steel for use in automotive related industries such as assembly plants, and metal for foodstuff containers. Steel requirements for these industries can generally be anticipated far enough in advance to allow sufficient time for shipment by boat. In Table 4.7, therefore, estimates of truck traffic have been revised assuming all steel products moving to Maracaibo and 50% of those destined to Maracay, Valencia, Caracas, Puerto Cabello, and Barquisimeto to be transported by ship. On the basis of these revised estimates the existing road via Ciudad Bolívar appears to be adequate at least until 1975 even without allowing for any change in over-all truck sizes. Between 1975 and 1980, total capacity of the regional routes

[24] For example, the cost per ton to Maracaibo estimated in Table 4–5 is Bs 70, whereas rates that have been quoted for this trip are Bs 194. The World Bank mission has calculated costs for the same trip at Bs 67 per ton and has suggested that this might be reduced to Bs 40 per ton. International Bank, *op. cit.*, pp. 457–458.

Table 4.7. Estimated Average Daily Truck Traffic between Ciudad Guayana and Selected Points Showing Capacity Requirements Assuming Some Domestic Steel Products Are Transported by Ship

Traffic Between Ciudad Guayana and	1966		1970		1975		1980	
	1000 Tons	Daily Two-Way Trucks	1000 Tons	Daily Two-Way Trucks	1000 Tons	Daily Two-Way Trucks	1000 Tons	Daily Two-Way Trucks
Maturín	33	14	74	31	158	66	283	119
El Tigre	24	10	58	24	124	52	227	95
Guarico	5	2	8	3	14	6	22	9
Puerto La Cruz	35	15	68	29	159	67	282	118
Caracas[1]	131	55	269	113	552	232	936	393
Maracay[1]	40	17	69	29	131	55	203	85
Valencia[1]	110	46	252	106	493	207	839	352
West of Valencia	25	10	40	17	68	29	103	43
Puerto Cabello[1]	15	6	23	10	39	16	53	22
Barquisimeto	2	1	5	2	10	4	19	8
Valera	16	7	38	16	86	36	158	66
Barinas	19	8	45	19	101	42	185	78
Apure	4	2	6	3	11	5	17	7
Maracaibo[2]	13	5	35	15	87	36	147	62
Total	472	198	990	417	2033	853	3474	1457
Required two-lane roads								
at 90 trucks/hr		1		1		2		2
at 140 trucks/hr		1		1		1		2

1 50% of steel products assumed to be transported by ship. 2 100% of steel products assumed to be transported by ship.

would have to be increased *either* by widening the Ciudad Guayana–El Tigre road *or* by replacing ferry service across the Orinoco at Ciudad Guayana with a bridge connection to the Los Barrancos highway.

In Table 4.8, estimates of total ship and highway tonnages are summarized for commodity flows between Ciudad Guayana and other locations in Venezuela if a highway-dominant transportation plan were in effect.

Railroad-Dominant Plan

This plan includes the construction of a railroad from Naricual to Matanzas in addition to a rail line from iron mines at San Isidro to the Orinoco Mining Company railroad. The economic justification of the Naricual-Matanzas railroad depends upon the relationship between the savings in variable costs of transportation obtained by using the railroad and the costs of amortizing the capital investment in the railroad line and rolling stock. Since the railroad would be owned and operated by the government, interest is confined to determining whether or not investment in railroad construction represents an efficient way for the government to spend available funds. Thus we are concerned with cost differentials between alternative modes of transportation and not revenues, whereas the private investor is interested primarily in the latter. On the other hand, savings in highway investment that may occur as a result of railroad construction can be taken into account, whereas the private investor has no interest in these.

An analysis of the proposed Naricual-Matanzas railroad, therefore, must consider differences in the costs of transporting goods to and from Ciudad Guayana by railroad, highway, and ship. For bulk quantities, such as coal from Naricual and limestone from Pertigalete, the relevant comparison is between railroad and ship, since ship costs are much lower than trucking costs for these commodities. For general cargo, the costs of moving goods via railroad from Ciudad Guayana to El Tigre or Puerto La Cruz and from there by truck must be compared with costs of shipping and trucking to various destinations in

107

Table 4.8. Estimated Distribution of Commodity Flows between Truck and Ship for Traffic between Ciudad Guayana and Selected Points

Traffic Between Ciudad Guayana and	Commodity Flows in 1000 Metric Tons							
	1966		1970		1975		1980	
	Truck	Ship	Truck	Ship	Truck	Ship	Truck	Ship
General Cargo								
Maturín	33	—	74	—	158	—	283	—
El Tigre	24	—	58	—	124	—	227	—
Guárico	5	—	8	—	14	—	22	—
Puerto La Cruz	35	—	68	—	159	—	282	—
Caracas	131	65	269	154	552	318	936	581
Maracay	40	12	69	28	131	57	203	105
Valencia	110	54	252	129	493	267	839	487
West of Valencia	25	—	40	—	68	—	103	—
Puerto Cabello	15	1	23	3	39	5	53	10
Barquisimeto	2	2	5	5	10	11	19	20
Valera	16	—	38	—	86	—	158	—
Barinas	19	—	45	—	101	—	185	—
Apure	4	—	6	—	11	—	17	—
Maracaibo	13	76	35	182	87	376	147	687
Total	472	210	990	501	2033	1034	3474	1890
Bulk Cargo								
Coro	—	140	—	140	—	350	—	700
Margarita	—	—	—	—	—	100	—	100
Guanta	—	680	—	1470	—	2740	—	4860
Total	—	820	—	1610	—	3190	—	5660

Venezuela. In this case, savings in operating costs on the railroad result from lower line-haul costs per ton-kilometer (approximately Bs 0.05 versus Bs 0.12 by truck). These savings, however, are reduced by the additional costs of transshipment at El Tigre or Puerto La Cruz.

In Table 4.9, costs of shipping general cargo between Ciudad Guayana and selected cities are summarized for ship, truck, railroad (freight car), and trailer-on-flat-car (piggy-

Table 4.9. Comparison of Portal-to-Portal Transportation Costs between Ciudad Guayana and Selected Cities by Ship, Road, and Railroad
in bolivars per ton[1]

Destination	Ship[2]	Truck[3]	Naricual-Matanzas Railroad	
			Piggyback[4]	Other[5]
General Cargo				
El Tigre	—	34.1	25.5	32.2
Puerto La Cruz	58.0	56.6	38.7	40.4
Caracas	69.0	96.5	83.3	85.0
Maracay	81.6	98.0	89.3	96.0
Valencia	75.6	102.7	94.4	101.1
Puerto Cabello	68.8	109.7	101.1	107.8
Barquisimeto	89.6	125.2	117.0	123.7
Barinas	118.8	146.7	137.5	144.2
Valera	103.6	154.7	145.5	152.2
Maracaibo	77.7	164.2	155.4	162.1
Maturín	—	28.8	61.6	67.8
Bulk Cargo				
Naricual	9.86	—	—	7.17
Pertigalete	8.12	—	—	7.62

[1] *1959 prices.*

[2] Fully distributed average costs including amortization of investment in ships and terminal charges.

[3] Fully distributed operating costs including terminal charges but excluding any allowance for road construction or maintenance costs.

[4] Trucking component as per footnote 3. Rail costs are operating costs only, exclusive of any allowance for investment in railroad construction or rolling stock but including terminal charges.

[5] Operating costs only as per footnote 4 above.

back) operations. Costs of transporting bulk cargoes from Nari-cual and Pertigalete by rail and ship are also shown. Railroad cost calculations are found in Appendix F. (p. 155). Note that in the case of ship and truck operations, costs are fully dis-tributed average costs including the costs of amortizing invest-ment in ships and trucks (but not roads), whereas railroad costs include only costs of operation. Cost savings must, there-fore, be compared with equipment costs as well as investment in construction.

These figures show that costs of transporting general cargo to various cities in Venezuela are much lower by ship than by railroad-truck alternatives. For all but goods destined to Maturín, however, rail-truck combinations represent a lower cost solution than trucking alone, although in most cases dif-ferences are insignificant in view of the uncertainties asso-ciated with the basic cost data. Rail costs are also lower for the bulk commodities shown, although in the case of limestone a small change in terminal costs could reverse the saving in favor of shipping. Thus, for general cargo, the railroad would be competitive at best only for the truck traffic estimated under the highway dominant plan, as summarized in Table 4.8. Some general cargo would continue to move by truck despite lower rates which could be offered by the rail-truck combina-tion. Traffic in this category would include very small ship-ments and high-value cargo for which the prospects of an overnight trip to Caracas or Valencia as opposed to two or three days by rail would outweigh the cost advantages of rail transportation. It has been assumed here that 20% of the general cargo not going by ship would be transported by truck despite the higher costs involved.

Railroad cost savings depend upon the distribution of traffic between freight car and piggyback operations. Since piggyback costs are lower for the proposed route, it would be advan-tageous to move as much cargo as possible by this method. For some cargo, side loading of flat cars will be necessary, as opposed to end loading of trailers. This cargo is assumed to range from one-quarter to one-half of all rail traffic, or 20 to 40% of total overland general cargo. For these traffic distributions and using cost differentials of Table 4.9, annual savings in transport costs are estimated in Table 4.10. These savings can be compared with railroad construction costs.

Construction cost estimates for the Naricual-Matanzas railroad are shown in Table 4.11. Because of the wide range in costs which have been estimated for this line, both low and high estimates are shown. Cumulative estimates showing the total investment which would have to be accumulated in rolling stock as of the various years are also shown. In Table 4.12, these initial costs have been converted into annual costs for interest rates of 4 to 10%. In computing the capital recovery factor at each interest rate, the life of the railroad facility itself has been assumed to be 35 years. Equipment lives vary depending upon the type of equipment and section of the route over which it is used. Flat cars running between Ciudad Guayana and El Tigre, for example, are estimated to have longer lives than similar equipment moving to Puerto La Cruz, since the average daily distance traveled will be less. Equipment life calculations are shown in Appendix F.

A comparison of Tables 4.10 and 4.12 indicates that before 1980 annual savings are much less than annual costs for the interest rates shown. In 1980, savings are equivalent to annual costs for the low construction cost estimates at an interest rate between 4 and 5%. In other words, if low construction costs are assumed, traffic volumes predicted for 1980 are sufficient to provide an internal rate of return of 4 to 5% on the investment in the railroad. When an allowance is made for saving a bridge crossing to Los Barrancos or widening of the road to El Tigre, the return on the low construction cost estimate increases to between 6 and 7% for 1980. In either case, the return on the investment is extremely low for a capital-scarce developing region. In view of the risks associated with such an undertaking, there would be little justification for constructing the railroad prior to the 1975–1980 period even if a return of 6 or 7% were to be considered acceptable. There are several reasons for this conclusion.

In the first place, the range of construction cost estimates is too broad to place any reasonable degree of confidence on the

Table 4.10. Summary of Estimated Annual Savings in Transportation Costs Resulting from Construction of the Naricual-Matanzas Railroad[1]

Savings Between Ciudad Guayana and Indicated Center	Savings in Bolivars/Ton	Total Savings in Bs 1000/Year		
		1970	1975	1980
Bulk Cargo Savings				
Naricual	2.81	2,360	4,440	7,620
Pertigalete	0.50	330	600	1,120
Subtotal		2,690	5,040	8,740
General Cargo Savings Alternative A[2]				
Caracas	9.88	2,660	5,450	9,250
Maracay	4.28	300	560	870
Valencia	3.96	1,000	1,950	3,320
Puerto Cabello	4.20	100	160	220
Barquisimeto	3.88	20	40	70
Barinas	4.68	210	470	870
Valera	4.68	180	400	740
Maracaibo	4.36	150	380	640
Puerto La Cruz	13.64	930	2,170	3,850
El Tigre	4.20	240	520	950
Subtotal		5,790	12,100	20,780
Alternative B[3]				
Caracas	10.22	2,740	5,620	9,520
Maracay	5.62	390	740	1,140
Valencia	5.30	1,340	2,620	4,450
Puerto Cabello	5.54	130	220	290
Barquisimeto	5.22	30	50	100
Barinas	6.02	270	610	1,120
Valera	6.02	230	520	950
Maracaibo	5.70	200	500	840
Puerto La Cruz	13.98	950	2,220	3,920
El Tigre	5.54	320	690	1,260
Subtotal		6,600	13,790	23,590
Total Savings				
Alternative A		8,480	17,140	29,520
Alternative B		9,290	18,830	32,330

[1] *1959 prices.*
[2] 50% of rail cargo by piggyback.
[3] 75% of rail cargo by piggyback.

Table 4.11. Summary of Estimated Investment Required in Construction and Rolling Stock for Naricual-Matanzas Railroad as of Selected Years

Items	Costs in 1000 Bolivars[1]	
	Low	High
Construction Costs		
240 km Llanos	168,000	312,000
98 km Mountains	93,100	245,000
Subtotal	261,100	557,000
Bridge across Orinoco	60,000	60,000
Terminal Facilities	9,000	9,000
Total Construction	330,100	626,000
Cumulative Costs—1970		
Locomotives	6,600	13,800
Ore Cars	18,700	18,700
Freight Cars	21,400	21,400
Total Rolling Stock	46,700	53,900
Total Rolling Stock plus Construction	376,800	679,000
Cumulative Costs—1975		
Locomotives	12,000	25,600
Ore Cars	34,800	34,800
Freight Cars	44,300	44,300
Total Rolling Stock	91,100	104,700
Total Rolling Stock plus Construction	421,200	730,700
Cumulative Costs—1980		
Locomotives	19,400	41,400
Ore Cars	61,700	61,700
Freight Cars	75,700	75,700
Total Rolling Stock	156,800	178,800
Total Rolling Stock plus Construction	486,900	804,800

[1] *1959 prices.*

113

Table 4.12. Estimated Annual Fixed Charges on Investment in Construction and Rolling Stock, Naricual-Matanzas Railroad for Selected Years and Interest Rates[1]

Annual Charges	High Estimates in Bs 1000			Low Estimates in Bs 1000		
	1970	1975	1980	1970	1975	1980
4% Interest						
Construction	19,460	19,460	19,460	36,910	36,910	36,910
Locomotives	850	1,560	2,530	1,810	3,330	5,400
Other Rolling Stock	3,420	6,700	11,680	3,420	6,700	11,680
Total	23,730	27,720	33,670	42,140	46,940	53,990
6% Interest						
Construction	26,190	26,190	26,190	49,680	49,680	49,680
Locomotives	930	1,710	2,770	1,990	3,640	5,920
Other Rolling Stock	3,960	7,760	13,520	3,960	7,760	13,520
Total	31,080	35,660	42,480	55,630	61,080	69,120
8% Interest						
Construction	34,000	34,000	34,000	64,450	64,450	64,450
Locomotives	1,010	1,860	3,020	2,170	3,980	6,450
Other Rolling Stock	4,520	8,880	15,460	4,520	8,880	15,460
Total	39,530	44,740	52,480	71,140	77,310	86,360
10% Interest						
Construction	42,780	42,780	42,780	81,140	81,140	81,140
Locomotives	1,100	2,030	3,290	2,350	4,330	7,020
Other Rolling Stock	5,120	10,070	17,530	5,120	10,070	17,530
Total	49,000	54,880	63,600	88,610	95,540	105,690

[1] 1959 prices.

114

estimated return. The use of average figures, such as Bs 700,000 or Bs 1,300,000, is unsatisfactory when a specific railroad line is under consideration. A preliminary survey would have to be made of the proposed alignment, earthwork computations carried out, and cost estimates made on the basis of actual quantities. Cost estimates obtained in this manner could then reasonably be expected to fall within 10% of real costs.

Second, the differences between shipping and railroad transportation costs for coal and limestone are too small in view of the uncertainties involved in these estimates.[25] A small change in terminal or transshipment costs or in the initial cost of the ships themselves could upset the balance in favor of shipping.

Third, uncertainty as to future volumes is also very great, as discussed previously. If this uncertainty is reflected by the use of higher interest rates, then the annual costs of the railroad will be considerably higher than the annual savings for those traffic estimates. While this uncertainty exists for the highway-dominant plan as well, the risks involved are much smaller. In the case of the railroad, an investment of the order of Bs 360 to Bs 660 million is needed just to go into operation, whereas under the highway-dominant plan, the necessary investment in roads has already been made, and further investment in trucks and ships can be made in accordance with traffic increases.

On the other hand, the possibility does exist that construction costs will be much lower than Bs 700,000 per kilometer used as a minimum here. Single-track construction costs in the United States have been estimated at approximately Bs 390,000 per kilometer ($140,000 per mile).[26] In the event that port charges continue to rise and lower shipping rates are not forthcoming, the railroad might attract much of the traffic estimated here to be moved by water transportation, thereby increasing the annual savings over truck transportation. In addition, the advent of new forms of technology, such as dual-purpose con-

[25] In fact, estimates made by the World Bank indicate shipping costs to be cheaper even when the channel toll for the Orinoco River is included. See International Bank, *op. cit.*, pp. 454–456.

[26] William W. Hay, *An Introduction to Transportation Engineering* (New York: John Wiley & Sons, Inc., 1961), p. 386.

tainers equipped with both flanged steel wheels and rubber tires, might add to the flexibility of the railroad by greatly facilitating transshipment from rail to road, and reducing rolling stock requirements.

In any event, the lead time for planning and construction necessary before the proposed railroad could be brought into operation would be about eight years. Thus, even if the decision to build the Naricual-Matanzas line were delayed until 1972, the railroad could be in operation by the time suggested here as the time when it might be first justified economically. Such a decision then would necessarily rest on a thorough review of the situation, including a more reliable evaluation of construction costs and a comparison of actual interregional commodity flows with those predicted for the same period. In view of the latter, revised estimates of potential railroad traffic could then be made for the period 1975–1980.

Investment Requirements

On the basis of the preceding analysis, the least-cost combination of transportation modes for accommodating interregional commodity flows generated by the Guayana industrial complex appears to be one in which most commodities are transported by truck and ship-truck combinations. The economic feasibility of further rail construction in the form of the proposed Naricual-Matanzas railroad is considered too risky at the present time to justify its inclusion in a regional transportation plan.[27]

---

[27] This conclusion does not seem overly conservative in view of the uncertainties involved in the commodity flow estimates, as lower production levels would show the rail alternative to be even less favorable. This view is not shared by all members of the economic planning staff, however, as the following quotation illustrates:

The implications of the projected Guayana outputs would seem to preclude the exclusive use of highway and water transportation. While water provides low transportation costs it does not reach many of the industrializing areas of the country and for transporting some heavy items connecting rail lines between the coast and the interior would be needed.

George Perazich, *Preliminary Program of Potential Industrial Development Projects for the Guayana Region* (Caracas: Corporación Venezolana de Guayana, 26 March 1962), p. 6 (mimeographed).

Major investments required to accommodate interregional commodity flows shown in Table 4.8 have been summarized in Table 4.13. Estimates for the second bridge over the Orinoco

Table 4.13. Estimated Investment Requirements in Major Interregional Transportation Facilities *in 1000 bolivars*[1]

Items	1963–66	1966–70	1970–75	1975–80
Highway Transportation				
Strengthening El Tigre Road	—	47,400	—	—
Paving Los Barrancos– Templador Road	—	—	15,300	—
Bridges Across Orinoco	120,500	—	—	138,500
Investment in Trucks	111,500	124,100	289,900[2]	413,000[3]
Total Highway	232,000	171,500	305,200	551,500
Water Transportation				
Ships	28,800	28,800	57,600	96,000
Total Investment	260,800	200,300	362,800	647,800

[1] *1959 prices.*
[2] Includes replacement of 1963–1966 investment.
[3] Includes replacement of 1966–1970 investment.

River are very preliminary as the location of this crossing has yet to be determined. This bridge is discussed in more detail in Appendix G (p. 158).

Although the investment requirements shown in Table 4.13 are based on high estimates of production and correspondingly high estimates of traffic volumes, it should be pointed out that they are not very sensitive to changes in the basic projections of regional output. The net effect of reductions in traffic estimates on the transportation needs of the region is actually very small. Investment in roads, for example, would be unaffected because existing highway capacity is already more than adequate. Economic justification of the bridge at Ciudad Bolívar would be affected to some extent, but this bridge appears to be one that could be justified on other than economic grounds in any event.

Lower traffic volumes would affect the investment needed in transportation equipment. Generally, however, trucks are acquired in accordance with traffic increases, and there is thus little risk of overinvestment in this area. Similarly, as mentioned earlier, lead time for the construction of the second bridge over the Orinoco River would be sufficient to make allowances for changes in commodity flow trends. The major transportation investments to be made in order to accommodate commodity flows generated by the planned Guayana industrial complex are therefore not seriously affected by the uncertainties involved in the basic projected regional outputs.

SOME IMPLICATIONS OF
THE CASE STUDY

Chapters Two and Three have presented a conceptual framework for analyzing the degree of factor substitutability possible in producing transportation. An attempt has been made to indicate the importance of considering a wide range of technology in planning transportation for developing regions as well as to illustrate the nature of the substitutability possible among various factors that go into the production of transport. It has been shown that different technologies are synonymous with different combinations of fixed investment and current costs and that the appropriate level of investment depends upon relative factor prices. Thus the level of investment (as expressed by the choice of design standards) that is in keeping with "best engineering practice" in one country may not be justified in another characterized by different relative factor prices. Because the differences in the relative factor costs are more pronounced among underdeveloped countries, the method of determining appropriate investment levels suggested here is likely to be more meaningful in such countries.

Some of the difficulties raised should have made it apparent that the total number of alternative technologies is probably greater than can reasonably be handled computationally. Thus the judgment and experience of the engineer, aided by recent improvements in computational techniques, must be relied upon to select the more relevant alternatives for consideration. However, the data presented in Chapter Three do illustrate how relatively scant cost information can be used to estimate the cost relationships relevant to the method of analysis.[1] While any sort of economic analysis requires some estimate of costs, the data requirements of the methods described do not appear to pose any special problems.

On the basis of the case study, several conclusions can be drawn pertaining to the specific case of the Guayana region and to the generality of some of the theoretical developments for transportation planning in other developing areas.

In analyzing the transport needs of the Guayana region, commodity flows developed in Chapter Four formed the basis for the various estimates that have been presented. For a variety of reasons, preliminary estimates of the demand for final goods and services produced in the Guayana region made by the project economists were based on analyses of historical consumption patterns. These showed the trend in the per capita consumption of various goods and services in Venezuela with changes in income. Price effects were neglected entirely. Changes in per capita consumption were thus attributed entirely to changes in income. While the validity of this procedure might be questioned, it should be pointed out that most of the commodities scheduled to be produced in the Guayana region are basic, non–consumer-oriented goods, most of which are now imported. Some minimum demand for such goods (the bulk of which are required as inputs for intermediate and consumer-oriented industries), can thus almost be guaranteed, regardless of price, by a government policy to ban further imports of similar goods.[2]

---

[1] These cost data were collected by the author over a period of three to four months. A national, familiar with local practice and working in his own country, could undoubtedly seek out the best sources of data in even less time. Moreover, a much wider range of data could readily be obtained in a shorter period of time using some of the computer techniques available for evaluating construction and road user costs. See for example, Paul O. Roberts and A. Villaveces, *A Digital Terrain Model (DTM) Design System*, (Cambridge: Department of Civil Engineering, Massachusetts Institute of Technology, 1963), Research Report R62-6 and A. S. Lang and D. H. Robbins, "A New Technique for Predicting Vehicle Operating Cost," *Operational Effects of Design and Traffic Engineering* (Washington: Highway Research Board, 1962), pp. 19–35, Bulletin 308.

[2] The demand for goods produced in the region may still retain a significant degree of price sensitivity if the possibility of producing similar goods in other regions of the country is considered. In this case, determining the demand for

Implicit in these demand estimates are all the uncertainties involved in the basic projections of regional consumption and production. It has been suggested, then, that transportation needs of the region should periodically be reviewed in the light of comparisons between observed trends and those of the original projections.

An important problem suggested by this analysis that might profitably be considered by the development agency concerns shipping rates. Lower shipping rates, consistent with the low real costs of this mode of transportation, may have important effects on the growth of the region. By lowering rates, delivered prices of regional outputs are also lowered, which in turn leads to greater demand for the products of the region. Similarly, shipping rates affect the cost of living in the region through their effect on import prices, which eventually affect costs of production. The availability of low-cost shipping can thus play an important role in any program of industrial promotion for the region.

Lower rates might be obtained by pricing regional outputs such as steel products f.o.b. La Guaira, Puerto Cabello, or Maracaibo. In this manner sufficient ship cargo might be guaranteed to permit lower rate schedules that in turn should lead to more traffic for this mode of transportation. Attempts could also be made to reduce the high port handling charges now associated with water transportation in Venezuela. In particular, methods of eliminating the cumbersome customs regulations governing the transportation of domestic goods by water should be investigated.

One of the more important conclusions pertaining to the particular case at hand is that, unlike most developing regions,[3]

---

final goods and services produced in the Guayana would require a thorough analysis of the locational advantage or competitive position that the Guayana region enjoys over other regions for the production of these commodities. A series of comparative cost studies for *each prospective industry* would be essential in analyzing the industrial growth potential of the region. See Walter Isard et al., *Methods of Regional Analysis: An Introduction to Regional Science* (New York: John Wiley & Sons, Inc., 1960), p. 233.

[3] In a paper presented at a recent conference on transportation economics, for example, Louis Lefeber has estimated that investment in transportation plant annually ranges from 20 to 50% of all scheduled investments in develop-

the lack of adequate transportation facilities does *not* represent a bottleneck to the economic development of the Guayana region. Some facilities, such as the bridge over the Orinoco River and the railroad spur to San Isidro, will be required in the near future. By and large, however, improvements to the basic regional transportation system can be scheduled as the need arises and can be carried out by the government agencies normally charged with this responsibility. In fact, existing highways and deepwater shipping facilities are more than adequate to satisfy the transportation needs of the region during the planning period under consideration. Some increase in port capacity along the northern coast may be necessary, although such increases could probably be obtained through administrative changes and improvement in the efficiency of port operations. With the exception of obtaining lower shipping rates, therefore, planning of regional transportation facilities appears to be one area with which the development agency need not be greatly concerned during the next five to ten years.

The case study also leads to some conclusions that may have general relevance to transportation planning in underdeveloped regions. In the case of the Guayana, for example, transport problems appear to be more administrative in kind than physical. Failure to mobilize excess capacity in the shipping industry through a proper pricing policy may yet lead to excessive investment in other modes of overland transportation.[4] Aside from this unwarranted investment, failure of the rate structure to reflect true transport costs may ultimately introduce distortions into the spatial pattern of economic activity. In cases where these administrative problems are so apparent, some sort of government policy of subsidy may be desirable

---

ment programs. See his *Economic Development and Regional Growth* (New York: National Bureau of Economic Research Inc., 26 April 1963), p. III-10 (mimeographed).

[4] Another example of poor transport administration is the case of ore boats that now carry iron ore from the Guayana region to the United States. These may not be used to carry return loads to Venezuela or to engage in domestic coastal transportation. By using these ships to transport coal and limestone from Guanta on the northern coast to the steel mill, transport costs for iron ore as well as for coal and limestone could be reduced.

in order to reduce the social cost of transportation. Examples from other countries indicate that such administrative difficulties (namely, bringing rates into line with economic costs) may well be characteristic of developing countries in general.[5]

Although the analysis here has been concerned primarily with road transportation, much of what has been said pertaining to the substitutability of inputs is applicable to other modes of transportation as well. In the case of railroads, for example, rail gauge is the key to a whole range of technological alternatives.[6] Narrow-gauge railroads permit the use of greater curvature and consequently construction costs are lower (notably with respect to earthwork and railroad ties). At the same time, however, the allowable rigid wheel base of the locomotive is reduced and this in turn restricts its hauling power. The size of train crews, on the other hand, remains constant. Thus the labor component of operating costs per ton-kilometer is greater than for broad-gauge track.

In a similar manner, reductions in initial fixed costs can be obtained through the use of lightweight rail. These initial cost savings, however, are made at the expense of increased operating costs because lighter trains must be run, and because at high speed annual maintenance-of-way expenditures increase.[7]

Other possibilities for substitution also exist within railroad transportation. Track capacity can be improved through the

[5] In India, for example, the improper location of many important industries has been attributed to poor transport administration and distortive pricing. See Lefeber, *op. cit.*, pp. III-15 ff.

[6] Substitution possibilities resulting from the selection of rail gauge may not be very meaningful, however, where rail facilities already exist due to the losses in system flexibility that would be occasioned by having more than one gauge. Holmstrom has stated rather emphatically:

Whatever the arguable merits . . . where a standard gauge exists, any engineer . . . who causes a railway to be built to a different gauge assumes a moral responsibility of the gravest order. Future generations are likely to curse him. J. Edwin Holmstrom, *Railways and Roads in Pioneer Development Overseas, A Study of Their Comparative Economics* (London: P. S. King and Son, 1934), p. 100.

[7] One study estimates that replacing 60-pound rail with 70-pound rail results in a saving of approximately 30% in annual maintenance-of-way expenditures. See *Rehabilitation of National Railroads of Colombia* (New York: Madigan-Hyland Corporation, 1956), p. 26.

acquisition of additional locomotives or through improvements in the track signal system, each alternative involving a different combination of labor, local capital, and foreign exchange components. Moreover, within the construction phase most of the labor-intensive alternatives possible in the construction of roads are also relevant. When all these alternatives have been analyzed, the various substitution possibilities for road-rail combinations (such as piggyback) can also be considered.

In the case of pipelines, technology is determined primarily by the combination of pipe diameter, pipe thickness, and the size and spacing of compressors. Isoquants can be drawn in terms of compressor horsepower and pipeline weight per unit distance, the optimum combination again being determined from the superposition of isocost curves. Curves showing the substitutability of current for fixed costs might also be used. In general, however, the labor component of operating costs is small, regardless of the method of operation employed. Thus the choice that is of greatest concern is among alternative combinations of capital inputs. The capacity of an existing pipeline, for example, might be expanded by adding additional pumping stations, by replacing the line with one of larger diameter, or by adding a second pipe.[8]

The range of substitutability possible for alternative transport modes varies for different phases of operation. In the case of terminal operations, for example, the possibilities depend largely on average shipment size; very large shipments can be handled using a wide range of machinery and manual methods, whereas small shipments will normally require manual handling. Thus one might reasonably expect the extent of possible substitution in terminal operations to be greatest for ship transportation and progressively less for rail and road transport. But in the construction and maintenance phases, substitution possibilities would be greatest for road and rail since either very labor-intensive or capital-intensive methods might be used.

[8] For a more complete discussion, see Richard B. Heflebower, "Characteristics of Transport Modes" in *Transport Investment and Economic Development*, Gary Fromm, ed. (Washington: The Brookings Institution, 1965), pp. 47–50.

For pipelines, minimum requirements for heavy machinery needed to handle pipe sections would be greater than for either road or rail. In the case of shipping, the route construction phase is limited to situations where channels are involved. The degree of factor substitutability possible in the line-haul operation phase might vary inversely as the size of the smallest unit that can be transported in view of the fact that these units can be moved individually or collectively (with a reduction in the unit labor component). In Table 5.1, an attempt has been

Table 5.1. Ranking of Alternative Transport Modes According to Degree of Factor Substitutability Possible in Various Phases of Operation

Construction of Route	Maintenance of Route	Line-Haul Operation	Terminal Operation
Road	Road	Road	Ship
Rail	Rail	Rail	Rail
Pipeline	Conveyor	Ship	Road
Conveyor	Pipeline	Conveyor	Conveyor
Ship	Ship	Pipeline	Pipeline

made to indicate the relative degree of factor substitutability possible in each of these phases of operation for several transport modes. Of all modes, belt conveyor systems of transportation probably offer the least degree of technological substitution, because their physical characteristics are primarily dependent upon terrain conditions and the nature of material to be transported.

Three important aspects of transportation planning have been omitted here that are beyond the scope of the present work. These concern methods of cost allocation, transport pricing policy, and the effect of transport investments on the over-all regional capital investment program.

For transport facilities that are characterized by joint use, there will be a need to determine methods of cost allocation. Comparisons of the costs of carrying freight by alternative modes of transportation, for example, may lead to erroneous conclusions unless those construction costs that are attributable to the facility's ability to accommodate freight-carrying vehicles can be isolated for each mode. This is particularly relevant in the case of road transportation where joint use by freight-carrying trucks and passenger-carrying busses and automobiles make it difficult to assign cost responsibility.[9]

The pricing of transportation services is another important question that has not been considered here. Pricing policy has been the subject of many contradictory arguments in the literature on transportation economics. The desirability of a cost-based rate structure, however, is one argument that has received wide acceptance among most authors in the field.[10] Such a rate structure enjoys a certain degree of appeal on the basis of equity, namely, that costs of providing a transport service should be borne by those to whom the benefits accrue, although in many cases the incidence of these benefits cannot be easily traced. A case can be made for cost-based rate structures, however, purely on the grounds of economic efficiency. Firms and households make their locational decisions on the basis of both production and transport costs, tending to select locations where the sum of these costs is minimized. These locational decisions, however, are based on money and not real costs. Thus, if transportation rate structures do not reflect true social costs, distortions are introduced into the spatial pattern of economic activity. In some cases, firms will locate at economically undesirable points while in other cases desirable locations will be overlooked.

The development of cost-based transportation rate structures has particular importance in less-developed countries where

[9] In the United States, there has been considerable interest in highway cost allocation studies. See for example, United States Congress, *Final Report on the Highway Cost Allocation Study,* House Document No. 54 (Washington: Government Printing Office, 1961).

[10] A cost-based rate structure is one in which rates bear some relationship to the cost of providing service. As opposed to this, value-of-service pricing employs a policy wherein rates are charged according to the value of the commodity moved.

transport investment and pricing policy are more crucial factors in economic development. Charging artificially high prices for transport (for example, charging average costs in an attempt to regain full costs) restricts interregional trade and the mobility of productive factors; but artificially low prices induce excess demand that may lead to unwarranted additional investment in the transport sector. Transport pricing problems in underdeveloped regions are further complicated by the fact that in addition to correcting the discrepancy between price of service and cost of service, the discrepancy between costs evaluated at market rates and those obtained from the use of shadow rates must first be corrected.[11]

Finally, the effect of transport investments on the over-all development program is another important consideration that has not been included in this work. The demand for freight transportation services depends upon total output of the region. This output in turn determines the need both for industrial inputs and for the consumer goods necessary to sustain populations engaged in productive activity. Total output, however, depends upon the capital available for investment once social overhead investments, including investments in transport, have been made. In part, these investment effects have not been considered because parallel studies of capital availability have not been made for the current Guayana industrial development program. Had such studies been under way, it might have been possible to investigate the opportunity cost of transport investments in terms of the returns forgone from alternative investments in other sectors.[12]

The implicit assumption throughout, therefore, has been

[11] For a further discussion of transport pricing and an introduction to the relevant literature, see James R. Nelson, "Pricing Transport Services" in *Transport Investment and Economic Development,* Gary Fromm, ed. (Washington: The Brookings Institution, 1965), pp. 195–223.

[12] Alternatively, the contribution to national income made by transport investments could be compared to the contribution made by investments in other sectors of the economy. One method of doing this is described by Brian V. Martin and Charles B. Warden, "Transportation Planning in Developing Countries," *Traffic Quarterly, XXIX,* 1, (January, 1965), pp. 59–75.

127

that marginal returns from investment in the transport sector were large enough to make some level of investment worth while in the first place. Proceeding from this assumption, the considerations that have been presented should shed some light on questions concerning the relative desirability of alternative modes of transportation and of alternative technologies within a mode, both as functions of transport demand. Hopefully, the relevant engineering information that is basic to the formulation of transportation policy in a developing country such as Venezuela has been indicated.

ESTIMATION OF THE RELATIVE IMPORTANCE OF ROAD CONSTRUCTION COST ELEMENTS FOR VARIOUS ROAD WIDTHS

The cost distributions shown in Table 3.2 are based on averages of all road types. The relative importance of each element, however, would vary from ōne road type to another, and some attempt should be made to take these variations into account.

Most of the data used to prepare Tables 3.2 and 3.3 are representative of a particular type of road constructed in Venezuela, known as Type C. Assuming the distribution of cost elements in Table 3.2 as indicative of this type of road, estimates of cost distributions for other road types can be made on the basis of the following arguments. Except in mountainous regions, changes in road width produce less than proportional changes in earthwork cross sections and thus earthwork quantities. For example, if the average height of cut is 1.5 meters for a roadway of 10.3 meters width, a 1% change in road width would produce approximately a ¾% change in the earthwork cross section (assuming side slopes of 2:1).[1] Site preparation costs, however, are proportional to increases in the width to be cleared, while drainage costs increase more than proportionally since culverts increase in both length and diameter. Increases

---

[1] Denoting by w, h, and s, width, average height of cut and side slope, respectively, $dw/w = w/(w + sh)$, where dw is the change in width.

in bridge costs, on the other hand, are less than proportional to increases in width since bridge costs depend primarily on the length of span and initial setup costs. Fencing costs are entirely independent of road width.

On the basis of those arguments, changes in each of the construction cost elements shown in Table 3.2 were assumed for each percentage change in road width.[2] Using these factors and taking Type C roads (with a width of 10.3 meters) as datum, new distributions of cost elements were made for other road types by (a) calculating changes in each element cost shown in Table 3.2 due to the change in road width, and (b) adjusting these changes proportionately so as to total 100%, and (c) computing new percentage distributions. These are shown in Table A.1 for road Types A, B, and D in llanos terrain.

Table A.1. Estimated Relative Importance of Road Construction Cost Elements for Various Road Widths (Llanos) *in Per Cent*

Cost Elements	Road Width in Meters			
	7.2	*10.3*	*14.6*	*21.3*
Preparation of Site	6.0	7.0	7.7	7.7
Earthwork	38.1	37.2	36.8	36.6
Culverts and Drainage	11.1	16.0	19.7	21.7
Base	6.6	7.7	8.5	9.0
Bridges	35.2	30.1	26.0	24.1
Fencing	3.0	2.0	1.3	0.9
Total	100.0	100.0	100.0	100.0

The distribution of costs shown in Table A.1 was then used to make estimates of labor, local currency, and foreign exchange components for each of the four road types considered, using the data of Table 3.3.

[2] Factors used per 1% change in width are for site preparation, 1.00%; earthwork, 0.75%; drainage, 1.25%; base, 1.00%; bridges, 0.50%; and fencing, 0.00%.

ESTIMATES OF TRANSPORT DEMAND
FOR THE GUAYANA REGION

a. The Demand for Industrial Inputs

Requirements for raw materials depend upon the processes used in the production of goods. In the case of steel production, several alternative methods of production are under consideration for future expansion of the existing steel mill, each of which differs significantly with respect to the inputs of coal, coke, and limestone necessary to produce one ton of finished steel. This variation in the coal and limestone requirements is particularly important since these components represent the major determinants to be considered in evaluating the feasibility of further railroad construction in the region.

The location of basic raw materials also has obvious transportation implications as it determines both the distance over which these materials must be moved (hence transport costs and competitive advantage of the region) and the mode of transport most likely to be used.

On the basis of the production targets shown in Table 4.2, estimates of the necessary quantities of input materials have been made for various target years. Input coefficients used for steel production were based on the steel production process currently in use together with estimates made by specialists as to future techniques that might be employed.

It should be recognized that considerable uncertainty may be involved in the use of constant input coefficients over future time periods. In some cases the assumption of constant coefficients is fairly safe, as in the case of aluminum production

131

where quantitative input-output relationships are described by exact equations. In the case of steel production, however, more scrap iron and steel may be introduced as the availability of steel products in Venezuela is increased.

Input data based on production targets for various years are summarized in Table B.1 to show the flow of goods into the

Table B.1. Primary Industrial Input Flows Entering Ciudad Guayana Based on Target Production Levels

Source	Alternative Modes of Transport	Annual Flow in 1000 Metric Tons			
		1966	1970	1975	1980
IRON ORE					
El Pao	Rail	6,000	6,000	6,000	6,000
Cerro Bolívar	Rail	14,000	14,000	14,000	14,000
San Isidro	Rail	2,100	12,900	28,000	31,000
Total		22,100	32,900	48,000	51,000
OTHER					
National					
Delta Amacuro	Ship	200	400	800	2,000
Eastern Guayana	Ship, Truck	—	—	290	550
Guacuripa	Truck–Rail Truck	324	724	1,340	2,390
Puerto La Cruz	Ship, Rail	—	—	28	70
Naricual	Ship, Rail	420	840	1,580	2,720
Pertigalete	Ship, Rail	281	631	1,130	2,080
Margarita	Ship	—	—	100	100
Coro	Ship	140	140	350	700
Other[1]	Truck, Rail	49	99	186	319
Foreign					
Western Europe	Ship	443	873	1,650	2,880
Eastern U.S.A.	Ship	106	222	422	713
South Africa[2]	Ship	34	68	132	229
West Indies[3]	Ship	200	400	800	2,000
Total (excluding iron ore)		2,197	4,397	8,808	16,751

[1] Scrap iron assumed to be divided equally among Maracaibo, Valencia, Caracas, and Puerto La Cruz.
[2] Alternate to Guacuripa and is therefore not included in total.
[3] Alternative to Delta Amacuro and is therefore not included in total.

proposed industrial center of Ciudad Guayana. Alternative modes of transportation that might be used in handling these flows are also indicated. Iron ore flows are shown separately because these will be handled by the special railroads already constructed for this purpose.

b. The Demand for Final Industrial Goods

Table 4.2 indicates that the bulk of the final goods expected to be produced in the Guayana region constitute input materials for other consumer-oriented industries as opposed to materials for direct consumption themselves. The demand for such products as basic metals, heavy machinery and equipment, and electrochemicals is therefore inherently linked in quantity to the demand for finished consumer goods that use these inputs, and in location to the areas where such goods are produced. In the case of finished steel products, for example, domestic demand will be created by many of the consumer-oriented industries located in the Caracas-Maracay-Valencia industrial belt. Except for structural steel and reinforcing rods that will have a large national market (the Guayana being the only source other than imports) the demand for construction will be limited to the local market, particularly during the early stages of the growth of the new city.

By using these industrial linkages, an attempt has been made to distribute those goods produced for domestic consumption to various points in the country. In some cases the appropriate distributions were fairly obvious, as for example, the distribution of petroleum equipment to oil-producing areas of the country or the distribution of steel for automotive uses to planned locations for auto assembly plants. In other cases, products were distributed according to national population distribution estimates in view of the per capita consumption estimates that had provided the basis for total output targets. A summary of these distributions is shown in Table B.2 for various target years of the development plan. As mentioned, market analyses of world demand provided the basis for the estimates of exports. The preponderance of furnace and rolling

Table B.2. Commodity Flows Originating in Ciudad Guayana

| | | 1966 Predictions in 1000 Metric Tons | | | | |
Destination	Iron Ore and Reduced Ore	Rolling Mill Products	Aluminum and Other Metals	Machinery and Equipment	Forest Products	Chemicals	Total Excluding Ore
Maturín	—	27	—	—	—	—	27
El Tigre	—	24	—	—	—	—	24
Barcelona							
(Puerto La Cruz)	—	8	—	—	—	—	8
Caracas	—	129	2	—	—	—	131
Maracay	—	23	—	—	—	—	23
Valencia	—	108	5	—	—	—	113
Puerto Cabello	—	2	—	—	—	—	2
Barquisimeto	—	4	—	—	—	—	4
Valera	—	16	—	—	—	—	16
Barinas	—	19	—	—	—	—	19
Maracaibo	—	76	1	—	—	—	77
Subtotals	—	436	8			—	444
Export	20,300	510	40			90	640
Totals	20,300	946	48			90	1,084

Table B.2. (continued)

1970 Predictions in 1000 Metric Tons

Destination	Iron Ore and Reduced Ore	Rolling Mill Products	Aluminum and Other Metals	Machinery and Equipment	Forest Products	Chemicals	Total Excluding Ore
Maturín	—	64	—	—	—	—	64
El Tigre	—	58	—	—	—	—	58
Barcelona							
(Puerto La Cruz)	—	19	—	4	—	—	23
Caracas	—	308	3	8	—	—	319
Maracay	—	55	—	—	—	—	55
Valencia	—	258	12	28	—	—	298
Puerto Cabello	—	5	—	—	—	—	5
Barquisimeto	—	10	—	—	—	—	10
Valera	—	38	—	—	—	—	38
Barinas	—	45	—	—	—	—	45
Maracaibo	—	182	2	8	—	—	192
Subtotals		1,042	17	48			1,107
Export	24,600	840	90	—		90	1,020
Totals	24,600	1,882	107	48		90	2,127

Table B.2. (continued)

Destination	Iron Ore and Reduced Ore	Rolling Mill Products	Aluminum and Other Metals	Machinery and Equipment	Forest Products	Chemicals	Total Excluding Ore
			1975 Predictions in 1000 Metric Tons				
Maturín	—	133	—	—	6	—	139
El Tigre	—	120	—	—	4	—	124
Barcelona (Puerto La Cruz)	—	39	—	8	3	—	50
Caracas	—	636	6	15	41	—	698
Maracay	—	114	—	—	6	—	120
Valencia	—	533	28	54	12	—	622
Puerto Cabello	—	10	—	—	—	—	10
Barquisimeto	—	21	—	—	—	—	21
Valera	—	79	—	—	7	—	86
Barinas	—	93	—	—	8	—	101
Maracaibo	—	376	4	15	21	—	416
Subtotals	—	2,154	33	92	108	—	2,387
Export	33,000	1,390	185	—	—	225	1,800
Totals	33,000	3,544	218	92	108	225	4,187

Table B.2. (continued)

	1980 Predictions in 1000 Metric Tons						
Destination	Iron Ore and Reduced Ore	Rolling Mill Products	Aluminum and Other Metals	Machinery and Equipment	Forest Products	Chemicals	Total Excluding Ore
Maturín	—	243	—	—	10	—	253
El Tigre	—	219	—	—	8	—	227
Barcelona (Puerto La Cruz)	—	72	—	10	6	—	88
Caracas	—	1,162	15	20	74	—	1,271
Maracay	—	209	—	—	10	—	219
Valencia	—	974	60	70	21	—	1,125
Puerto Cabello	—	19	—	—	—	—	19
Barquisimeto	—	39	—	—	—	—	39
Valera	—	145	—	—	13	—	158
Barinas	—	170	—	—	15	—	185
Maracaibo	—	687	10	20	38	—	755
Subtotals	—	3,939	85	120	195	—	4,339
Export	37,000	2,100	450	40	—	450	3,040
Totals	37,000	6,039	535	160	195	450	7,379

mill products as the major industrial output for the manufacture of final goods produced in the region in response to domestic demand is evident from this table.

c. The Demand for Consumer Goods

The third type of commodity flow that must be considered in determining the demand for transportation is the flow of consumer goods necessary to sustain regional populations of the expected magnitude. Characteristically such goods tax the terminal and distributive capacity of the transportation system more than the line-haul capacity.

In predicting the flow of consumer goods for a newly developing region such as the Guayana, the transportation planner is concerned with predicting both the total quantity of consumer goods that will flow into the region and the manner in which these goods will be distributed over the region. As before, transport demand is derived from the total demand for consumer goods and involves all the price and transport cost considerations already mentioned with respect to the demand for final industrial products. Predicting the demand for consumer goods in a region whose economic structure is expected to undergo serious modifications is necessarily complicated by the fact that consumer tastes change as incomes rise and, equally as important, as rural populations become urbanized (even without any change in real income). In addition, demand predictions for consumer goods can be complicated by more uncertainty as to the sources of commodities demanded. Here the problem is to determine to what extent needs can be satisfied by local production. In the case of food production, for example, new markets created by the expected increase in regional population may provide incentive for production on lands not presently under cultivation.

In the following sections predictions of consumer goods commodity flows are made for various target years. Nonfood and food consumption goods are treated separately, since methods for predicting each vary. Moreover, perishability represents an important consideration in dealing with the transportation of foodstuffs, a matter of little concern for non-food commodities.

1. *Nonfood consumer goods.* In view of the lack of adequate demand-price relationships, demand estimates for nonfood consumer goods were based on estimates of total consumer expenditures on manufactured goods for various target years.[1] Estimates of the number of workers who would be employed in the local production of consumer goods were also available which, when multiplied by production coefficients, gave estimated tonnages of each of the consumer goods to be produced in the new city. Finally, estimates were made of the percentages of total consumer goods, by commodity, that would be produced locally. Using these percentages, per capita tonnages of manufactured goods demanded in the city could be estimated (Table B.3).

Table B.3. Estimated Per Capita Consumption of Nonfood Consumer Goods in Ciudad Guayana

Commodity	Estimated Annual Consumption (*in Metric Tons Per Capita*)			
	1966	1970	1975	1980
Footwear and Clothing	.256	.258	.227	.223
Textiles	.005	.006	.008	.007
Furniture	.027	.056	.107	.107
Graphic Arts	.122	.083	.099	.098
Petroleum By-products	.020	.024	.024	.022
Others	.055	.049	.038	.032
Total	.485	.476	.503	.489

Per capita consumption figures were then used to estimate the total demand for consumer goods in the region (Table B.4). Because much of the local production of consumer goods will depend upon supplies of materials and semifinished prod-

[1] Joseph D. Phillips, *Consumption Estimates for Ciudad Guayana 1970 and 1980* (Caracas: Corporación Venezolana de Guayana, Joint Center-Guayana Project, 20 November 1962), File B-39, pp. 4–5 (mimeographed).

Table B.4. Estimated Origin and Distribution of Nonfood Consumer Goods Entering Bolívar State (*in metric tons*)

A. Distribution

Destination	Incoming Goods			
	1966	*1970*	*1975*	*1980*
Ciudad Guayana[1]	62,400	114,600	222,100	314,500
Ciudad Bolívar[2]	36,500	50,400	64,200	76,200
Other Urban Areas[3] greater than 2,500	12,100	14,100	17,300	19,600
Rural Areas[3]	32,000	32,500	35,100	34,600
Total	143,000	211,600	338,700	444,900

B. Origin

Origin[4]	Per Cent	Incoming Goods			
		1966	*1970*	*1975*	*1980*
Caracas–La Guaira	35	50,000	74,000	118,000	155,700
Maracay	20	28,600	42,300	67,700	89,000
Puerto Cabello	10	14,300	21,200	33,900	44,500
Puerto La Cruz	10	14,300	21,200	33,900	44,500
Valencia	25	33,800	52,900	84,800	111,200
Total	100	143,000	211,600	338,700	444,900

[1] Table B-3.
[2] Per cent imported of each commodity assumed similar to that of Cuidad Guayana in 1966.
[3] 80% of per capita consumption requirements assumed to be imported.
[4] Imported goods assumed to originate from La Guaira, Puerto Cabello, or Puerto La Cruz.

ucts from other regions, these estimates include an allowance of one ton of imported materials per ton of finished product produced locally. In addition, per capita consumption estimates of small urbanized and rural areas have been reduced to 80% of those for the major urban areas.

In Table B.4 an attempt has also been made to indicate the origins of these consumer goods (including inputs for local production). Although a portion of these goods will be imported from abroad, they would probably enter Venezuela through one of the northern seaports. All consumer goods entering the region were thus considered to originate from the Caracas-Maracay-Valencia industrial area or from the ports of Puerto Cabello, La Guaira, or Puerto La Cruz in the proportions indicated.

2. *Food consumption.* In determining the demand for food and beverages, an analysis of past trends can be used to estimate per capita food consumption figures. Although changes in consumer tastes for foods are likely to vary to a greater extent as income levels change than in the case of nonfood commodities, such changes are more likely to be qualitative (for example, the substitution of meats for root vegetables, or preferences for better cuts of meat), having relatively small effect on the tonnage of food demanded per person. Even though per capita tonnages may remain constant, however, changes in the type of food consumed can have important implications for transportation if these are accompanied by the need for specialized types of transport equipment (such as refrigerated trucks).

An attempt has been made to account for changes in consumer preference when deriving per capita consumption coefficients for food products. It was assumed, for example, that with the rising incomes expected in the future, increases in the consumption of meat, milk and milk products, vegetables, and fruits would be accompanied by corresponding decreases in the consumption of grains and other carbohydrates.[2] In addition, slight increases of total per capita consumption were expected to take place, going from 288 to 309 kilograms per person annually (excluding beverages) over the period 1960 to 1980.[3] These estimates provided the basis for estimates of total food consumption in the region.[4]

From the point of view of transportation considerations, the

[2] Lorand Dabasi-Schweng, *Food and the Industrial Development of the Guayana* (Caracas: Corporación Venezolana de Guayana, Joint Center-Guayana Project, 5 December 1962), pp. 22–23 (unpublished).

[3] *Ibid.*, p. 26.

[4] For a detailed breakdown of these totals into food types, see *ibid.*, p. 25.

real problem presented by the demand for food and beverages concerns determining what portion of this total demand will be met by local production and what portion will have to be imported. Lack of data on the agricultural potential of the region makes this a particularly difficult problem in the case of the Guayana.

Present agricultural production of the Guayana region is not large, partly because the land does not appear to be well suited to agriculture[5] and partly due to the lack of such development facilities as experimental farms, adequate extension service, and investment capital. With the expanding market for agricultural products anticipated in the near future, however, certain areas not now under cultivation may become economically viable due to any advantage in transport costs they might enjoy relative to other food-producing areas of the country. If large tracts of such land were to be brought into production, the estimated demand for the transport of foods to the region might be seriously overestimated. But without some fairly extensive agricultural surveys of the region, such estimates would be difficult to make.[6]

The kinds of studies that would be necessary in order to obtain better estimates of the demand for food transport are basically:

1. Surveys of soil conditions, rainfall, microclimate, and topographical features that could be composed as a series of overlays on a map of the region. (Using various shadings or other graphic techniques, the areas with greater agricultural possibilities would be high-lighted.[7]

[5] Estimates indicate yields per hectare in the Guayana region are below the national average (although higher than some other food-producing areas). *Ibid.*, p. 69.

[6] The difficulty of making agricultural estimates is illustrated by the following comment of Dr. Abel Sierra Cifuentes in a report to the Ministry of Agriculture, referring to milk production:

The characteristics of the region and the primitive state of the establishments in which . . . production . . . can be considered more an accident than rational habit, make it practically impossible to hazard an estimate . . . of the potentiality of the region for milk production.
Ibid., p. 71.

[7] For example, using progressively heavier shading to indicate improving soil conditions, etc., the best agricultural areas would show up as the darkest spots on the overlay system.

2. For the potential areas indicated by the surveys, studies of the yields and associated costs (including development costs) of producing different crops with different methods of production and management practices.

3. Studies of the costs of transporting agricultural products from these areas to potential markets over various types of roads.

On the basis of data obtained from these studies, contours could be constructed about each agricultural location indicating the total cost of various food products at different distances from the point of production. Intersections of equal cost contours for other localities would thus indicate the market area over which each would enjoy a competitive advantage, and in this manner preliminary estimates of the flow of foodstuffs could be determined. In addition to providing information on the commodity flow that can be expected, such studies are basic to any program for constructing a system of agricultural penetration roads.

In the absence of these studies, some estimates have been made concerning the proportion of food products imported into the region. In 1960, for example, food commodities imported into the region are estimated to have represented 20–25% of total consumption by the urban population.[8] This percentage is estimated to increase to about 50% by 1980 due to the expected growth in regional population, and barring any major program to increase the intensity of agricultural activity in the region.[9] Interpolating for the intermediate years, rough estimates of the flow of food products expected to enter the region from various points in Venezuela can be derived as shown in Table B.5.

Determining the distribution of these imported food products, however, is again complicated by the lack of detailed information on the agricultural potential of the region. The demand for these food imports in urbanized areas will undoubtedly be more than proportional to relative urban populations and, in fact, it would probably involve no great error

[8] Dabasi-Schweng, op. cit., p. 9.

[9] This estimate was made by Lorand Dabasi-Schweng, staff economist with the Corporación Venezolana de Guayana, Joint Center-Guayana Project.

Table B.5. Estimated Tonnages of Food Products Entering Bolívar State

Item	1966	1970	1975	1980
Total Food Consumption (excluding nonmilk beverages), *metric tons*	101,700	142,500	221,100	299,700
Per cent imported	31	37	43	51
Foods Imported (excluding nonmilk beverages), *metric tons*	31,500	52,800	95,300	151,500
Beverages Imported (at 45 liters/person), *metric tons*	14,600	21,300	32,000	42,700
Total Food and Beverages Imported, *metric tons*	46,100	74,100	127,300	194,200

Table B.6. Estimated Distribution of Imported Food Products Entering Bolívar State

A. *Distribution*

Destination	Annual Imports in Metric Tons			
	1966	1970	1975	1980
Ciudad Bolívar	8,300	13,400	22,900	34,900
Ciudad Guayana	31,300	50,700	86,600	132,100
Upata and South	6,500	10,000	17,800	27,200
Total	46,100	74,100	127,300	194,200

B. *Origin*

Origin	Annual Imports in Metric Tons			
	1966	1970	1975	1980
Apure	3,600	6,000	10,800	17,100
Eastern Guayana	400	700	1,200	2,000
Caracas	3,400	4,900	7,400	9,800
Guárico	4,600	7,700	13,900	22,100
Maturín	6,200	10,400	18,900	30,000
Valencia	3,400	4,900	7,400	9,800
West of Valencia	24,500	39,500	67,700	103,400
Total	46,100	74,100	127,300	194,200

to assume that all imported foods would be destined to the major urban areas of Ciudad Guayana, Ciudad Bolívar, and Upata. (In any event, imported foodstuffs consumed by the rural population would be acquired from one of these centers.) In Table B.6, Part A, imported foodstuffs have been distributed among the three urban areas in proportion to their relative population estimates. The distribution of food sources shown in Part B of the table is based on comparisons of the detailed breakdown of food consumption by type, cited earlier, with agricultural production data for other regions of the country.

ESTIMATED VENEZUELAN
SHIPPING COSTS

For general cargo, shipping costs are characterized by low line-haul costs and high terminal costs. As a result, the competitive advantage of shipping over other modes of transport increases for longer distances where the savings in line-haul costs may accumulate sufficiently to offset high terminal costs. Bulk commodities, on the other hand, are generally characterized by low terminal costs.

Line-haul shipping costs are composed of depreciation charges and the daily costs of operating and maintaining the vessel. Depreciation charges, of course, depend upon the initial cost of the ship, which is largely a function of ship type and tonnage capacity. For the bulk commodities such as coal and limestone entering the Guayana region, and for finished products such as steel tubes and structural steel leaving the region, bulk carriers of 10,000-ton capacity would probably be used. Although such ships would be used principally for transporting minerals, provisions could be made for the carriage of nonfragile finished steel products from the proposed industrial complex. A new 10,000-ton bulk carrier would cost around Bs 11,200,000 ($2.5 million U.S.). In the present shipping market, however, a vessel of this type might be acquired at prices as low as Bs 7,000,000. Estimated operating costs for such a vessel range from Bs 6,000[1] to Bs 11,000 per day. The

[1] Adapted from Sergio Sánchez Naranjo, *El Desarrollo Económico de la Región Suroriental y Los Transportes* (Caracas: Corporación Venezolana de Guayana, División de Estudios, Planificación e Investigación, 19 January 1962), p. 106.

latter figure corresponds to average United States costs.[2] An initial cost of Bs 9,600,000 and a daily operating and maintenance cost of Bs 8,600 steaming and Bs 6,800 in port have been used here.

In view of the heavy tonnages of coal and limestone anticipated for the future, larger vessels might come into use. A

Table C.1. Estimated Shipping Costs for 10,000-Ton Vessels[1]

Initial Cost in Bolivars	9,600,000
Annual Cost in Bolivars at 10% for 25-year Amortization Period	1,058,000
Daily Depreciation and Interest Charges (*in Bolivars*)	3,100
Daily Operating and Maintenance Charges (*in Bolivars*)	
Steaming	8,600
In Port	6,800
Total Daily Charges	
Steaming	11,700
In Port	9,900
Unloading Rate in Tons/Hour	
Bulk	700
General	100
Loading Rate in Tons/Hour	
Bulk	900
General	125
Terminal Costs in Bolivars/Ton	
Bulk Loading	0.45
Unloading	1.80
General Loading	6–10
Unloading	20–44

[1] *1959 prices.*

[2] Ralph E. Casey, "The Maritime Industry and its Problems," in *U.S. Transportation, Resources, Performance, and Problems,* Publication 841-S (Washington: National Academy of Sciences, 1961), p. 307, estimates average daily costs (excluding depreciation) to be $2,519 steaming and $2,030 in port.

20,000-ton ship is estimated to cost Bs 18,000 and would have daily operating costs of Bs 13,300 in steaming and Bs 10,600 in port.[3]

On the basis of these figures average daily charges for 10,000-ton ships are shown in Table C.1. An amortization period of 25 years has been assumed at 10% interest. Since most routine maintenance is carried out while the ship is under way, operation is assumed at 340 days per year.[4] Table C.1 also shows estimates of loading and unloading rates for bulk and general cargo as well as estimated terminal costs.

[3] This corresponds to an estimated $4 million initial cost and daily operating costs of $2,800. John R. Meyer, Merton J. Peck, John Stenason, and Charles Zwick, *The Economics of Competition in the Transportation Industries* (Cambridge, Mass.: Harvard University Press, 1959), p. 114.

[4] Allowing 25 days for lay-up overhaul and repairs, *ibid.*, p. 116.

ESTIMATED VENEZUELAN
RAILROAD COSTS

Due to the relatively small scale of railroad operations in Venezuela, estimates of constructing, maintaining, and operating railroads under Venezuelan conditions are difficult to obtain. Where estimates have been made, as by the National Railroad Commission (Comisión Economica Ferroviaria), they usually understate by a large amount the actual costs incurred in constructing recent railroads. For example, the Railroad Commission has estimated construction costs in llanos and mountainous terrain to be Bs 700,000 and Bs 1,100,000 per kilometer, whereas on the recently constructed Gran Ferrocarril Puerto Cabello, an average cost of Bs 1.7 million per kilometer was found. Other projects showed similarly high costs.[1]

Cost estimates for railroad construction in llanos and mountainous regions are shown in Table D.1. Instead of averages, the range of construction costs is shown for each case since initial costs are relatively more significant for the evaluation of railroad proposals than in the case of shipping. Differences in construction cost estimates will thus have a greater influence

[1] The 27-kilometer Guanta-Naricual railroad averaged Bs 2.6 million per kilometer including Bs 30 million for tunnels. Even excluding the tunnels, average costs exceeded Bs 1.5 million per kilometer. In the Guayana region, the Orinoco Mining Company's 146-kilometer railroad required an average investment of Bs 1.25 million per kilometer. Sergio Sánchez Naranjo, *El Desarrollo Económico de la Región Suroriental y Los Transportes* (Caracas: Corporación Venezolana de Guayana, División de Estudios, Planificación e Investigación, 19 January 1962), pp. 91–92.

Table D.1.   Estimated Costs of Railroad Construction
and Operation in Venezuela[1]

Construction Costs in Bolivars per Kilometer	
Llanos	700,000–1,300,000
Mountains	950,000–2,500,000
Equipment Costs in Bolivars	
Diesel Locomotive (1800 HP)	838,000–1,790,000
50-ton Ore Car	76,000
35-ton Box Car	66,000
35-ton Flat Car	58,000
Operating and Maintenance Costs in Bolivars/Ton-Kilometer	
Bulk Cargo	0.015–0.019
General Cargo	0.050
Terminal Costs in Bolivars/Ton per Handling	
Bulk Cargo	0.70
General Cargo	
Loading	6.0
Unloading	9.0

[1] *1959 prices.*

on both estimates of final total costs and the assignment of commodity flows to alternative modes.

Estimates of equipment costs and operating costs are also shown in Table D.1. Ranges are again used, particularly where there is a substantial difference between cost estimates and actual costs of equipment purchased during the last ten years. The low figure for bulk operating costs corresponds to experience on the two iron mining company railroads now operating in the Guayana region. Since these railroads carry no mixed traffic and operate with a high degree of efficiency, it is doubtful that bulk cargo costs on future government railroads that might be constructed in the region would be less than the amount shown.

Finally, in connection with these costs of rail transportation, costs of subsidiary operations, such as transshipment to trucks or the use of piggyback, are of interest. For piggyback operation, the Railroad Commission estimates a cost of Bs 15.65 to cover all terminal costs of handling a piggyback trailer including transfer to and from the flat car and costs of yard operation.[2] Costs of transferring general cargo from freight sheds to trucks depend primarily on the size of shipment. For the type of cargo expected to move to and from the Guayana region, these terminal costs are estimated to range from Bs 3.6 per ton to Bs 9.0 per ton per handling for average shipments of 11 and 5 metric tons, respectively.

[2] *Informe Económico Sobre Un Plan Ferroviario Nacional* (Caracas: Comisión Económica Ferroviaria, 1960), p. 189. This compares with U.S. estimates of $3.50 for loading and unloading and $0.30 for switching or a total of Bs 17.10. John R. Meyer et al., *The Economics of Competition in the Transportation Industries* (Cambridge, Mass.: Harvard University Press, 1959), p. 105.

151

CALCULATION OF SHIPPING COSTS
FROM CIUDAD GUAYANA
TO SELECTED VENEZUELAN PORTS

The estimated flow of bulk commodities from Coro, Margarita, Pertigalete, and Guanta is such that vessels used to carry these commodities to Ciudad Guayana would have sufficient capacity on the return trip to carry all outgoing finished steel products. Data in Chapter Four show, for example, that total incoming tonnages from the four ports just mentioned total 1,610 and 3,190 thousand metric tons for 1970 and 1975, respectively; outgoing flows which could be carried by ship to La Guaira (for Caracas), Puerto Cabello (for Maracay, Valencia, Barquisimeto, Barinas, and Puerto Cabello) and Maracaibo (for Maracaibo and Valera) total 900 and 1,860 thousand tons, respectively, for the same years. The required shipping capacity for these outgoing flows is thus roughly equal to one-half that needed to transport the incoming phosphates, magnesite, coal, and limestone.

In estimating shipping costs between these various ports, therefore, the first step is to determine the number of ships required for, and the costs associated with, the shipment of incoming bulk cargos. The additional costs of handling outgoing flows can then be determined. For these outgoing flows, we are interested only in the additional or incremental costs incurred by carrying such commodities, since certain costs would be incurred in any case in returning ships to their ports of embarkation. For purposes of making these calcula-

tions, it is assumed that ships leaving Pertigalete with limestone and coal would stop at Puerto Cabello and La Guaira
on the return trip from Matanzas, while ships from Coro and
Margarita would handle traffic destined to the port of Maracaibo. Cost calculations are shown in Table E.1 for 10,000-ton
vessels using the cost data of Table C.1 in Appendix C.

Table E.1. Calculation of Basic Shipping Costs for Bulk
Commodity Flows Destined to Ciudad Guayana
10,000-Ton Vessels[1]

Items	Guanta-Matanzas	Margarita-Matanzas	Coro-Matanzas
Round-Trip Distance in Nautical Miles	960	850	1720
Days Steaming at 10 Knots	4.0	3.6	7.2
Days in Port[2]	1.2	1.2	1.2
Total Cost Steaming[3] (Bolivars)	46,800	42,100	84,200
Total Costs in Port[3] (Bolivars)	11,900	11,900	11,900
Total Line-Haul Costs	58,700	51,000	96,100
Line-Haul Costs in Bolivars/Ton	5.87	5.41	9.61
Terminal Costs in Bolivars/Ton	2.25	2.25	2.25
Total Costs in Bolivars/Ton	8.12	7.66	11.86
Annual Trips per Ship	65	70	40
Annual Tonnage per Ship	650,000	700,000	400,000

[1] 1959 prices.
[2] 900 tons per hour loading, 700 tons per hour unloading, plus 15% for contingencies.
[3] See Table C.1.

In Table E.2, the additional costs of carrying general cargo
from Matanzas to Puerto Cabello, La Guaira, and Maracaibo
are shown. In returning to Guanta via Puerto Cabello and La
Guaira, for example, the additional distance is approximately
770 nautical miles, or an incremental steaming time of 3.2 days.
The cost of this additional steaming time is distributed between cargo destined to La Guaira and Puerto Cabello in
proportion to the total tonnage destined to each port (45%
and 55%, respectively). Tonnage destined to Puerto Cabello
includes commodities that will be transshipped from there to

Table E.2. Incremental Costs of Shipping General Cargo from Ciudad Guayana to Selected Venezuelan Ports for 10,000-Ton Vessels[1]

Items	Bulk Cargo Port		
	Guanta	Guanta	Coro
Destination	La Guaira	Puerto Cabello	Maracaibo
General Cargo per Trip	4,500	5,500	10,000
Incremental Steaming (days)[2]	1.4	1.8	2.8
Days in Port[3]	7.8	9.6	17.4
Steaming Cost in Bs	16,400	21,100	32,800
Port Costs in Bs	77,200	95,000	172,300
Total Line-Haul Costs in Bs	93,600	116,100	205,100
Line-Haul Costs in Bs/ton	9.4	11.6	20.5
Terminal Costs[4] in Bs/ton	50.0	50.0	50.0
Total Cost per ton	59.4	61.6	70.5
Total Circuit Time including Stop at Bulk Cargo Port	26	[5]	29
Annual Round Trips per Ship	13	13	11
Annual Tonnage per Ship			
General Cargo	58,500	71,500	110,000
Bulk Cargo	130,000	[5]	110,000

[1] *1959 prices.*
[2] La Guaira 45% and Puerto Cabello 55% of 3.2 days.
[3] Assumes 12-hour working day, loading rates shown in Table C.1, and 15% for contingencies.
[4] Assumes Bs 6 for loading and Bs 44 for unloading.
[5] Included under La Guaira.

Maracay, Valencia, Barquisimeto and Barinas. As the figures of Table E.2 indicate, the major component of incremental costs incurred in transporting general cargo results from daily ship operating charges while in port. Whereas time spent in port loading and unloading amounts to only 1.2 days for bulk cargo, 15.6 days are needed for general cargo. Ships returning via Puerto Cabello and La Guaira thus require a circuit time of 26 days, as opposed to only 5 days for ships returning directly to Guanta.

COST ESTIMATES FOR THE PROPOSED NARICUAL-MATANZAS RAILROAD

F.1 *Comparison of Estimated Costs of Transporting Coal and Limestone: Ship versus the Proposed Naricual-Matanzas Railroad*

The costs of transporting coal from Naricual and limestone from Guanta via the proposed Naricual-Matanzas railroad are estimated to be the following:

a. Coal from Naricual

Loading and unloading at Bs 0.70 per ton per handling	Bs 1.40
338 km at Bs 0.017 per ton-km	5.77
Total railroad costs	Bs 7.17

b. Limestone from Guanta

Loading and unloading cost per ton	Bs 1.40
365 km at Bs 0.017 per ton-km	6.22
Total railroad costs	Bs 7.62

The cost of carrying limestone from Guanta by ship has already been calculated (Appendix E) at Bs 8.12 per ton. Shipping costs for coal must include the cost of transporting coal from Naricual to the port at Guanta. Thus total shipping costs for coal are the following:

Loading and unloading cost	Bs 1.40
27 km at Bs 0.017 per ton-km	0.46
Shipping to Matanzas	8.12
Total shipping costs	Bs 9.98

Savings in operating cost obtained through using the railroad are, therefore, Bs 0.50 per ton for limestone and Bs 2.81 per ton in the case of coal.

F.2 Costs of Shipping General Cargo via the Proposed Naricual-Matanzas Railroad

In order to obtain costs of using the proposed Naricual-Matanzas railroad to ship general cargo between Ciudad Guayana and the rest of Venezuela, estimates of rail costs to El Tigre and Puerto La Cruz have been made for both freight car and piggyback operations. These are shown in Table F.1. These estimates include the cost of transshipment to trucks and unloading at final destinations. Therefore to arrive at total

Table F.1. Estimated Costs of Shipping General Cargo to El Tigre and Puerto La Cruz via the Proposed Naricual-Matanzas Railroad[1]

Items	Estimated Costs Between Ciudad Guayana and	
	El Tigre	Puerto La Cruz
Railroad Distance in Kilometers	201	365
Freight Car Costs in Bs/ton		
Line-Haul at Bs 0.05 per ton-km	10.05	18.25
Loading Costs in Bs/ton	6.00	6.00
Unloading Costs in Bs/ton	9.00	9.00
Truck Loading and Unloading at Bs 3.6/ton	7.20	7.20
Total Freight Car Costs	32.25	40.45
Piggyback Costs in Bs/ton		
Line-Haul at Bs 0.05 per ton-km	16.25	29.50
Terminal Charges in Bs/ton	1.97	1.97
Truck Loading and Unloading at Bs 3.6/ton	7.20	7.20
Total Piggyback Costs	25.42	38.67

[1] *1959 Bolivars.*

costs, only the line-haul costs computed at Bs 0.12 per ton-km from either El Tigre *or* Puerto La Cruz need be added to the figures shown in Table F.1.

Line-haul costs for piggyback operations are higher since the weight of the trailer itself must be included. In this case an average trailer capacity of 15.9 metric tons having a tare weight of 4.9 tons and operating with a 50% load factor has been assumed. Line-haul costs are thus computed on the basis of 25.7 tons per 15.9 tons of actual cargo. Terminal charges for loading *and* unloading a 15.9-ton trailer have been assumed to be Bs 15.65 per trailer.[1]

F.3 *Determination of Railroad Equipment Lives*

Total equipment life in years has been computed on the basis of estimated life in terms of kilometers and average annual utilization. Average locomotive life has been assumed to be $1,930 \times 10^3$ kilometers while averages of 885×10^3 kilometers have been assumed for other rolling stock. Equipment lives are summarized in Table F.2.

Table F.2. Estimated Lives of Rolling Stock Operating on the Proposed Naricual-Matanzas Railroad

Rolling Stock	Round Trips Per Year	Round Trip Distance	Life In Years
Locomotives			
Naricual-Guanta (Bulk)	285	700	10
Puerto La Cruz (General Cargo)	285	730	9
El Tigre (General Cargo)	430	400	11
Ore Cars			
Naricual-Guanta	120	700	10
Freight Cars			
Puerto La Cruz	66	730	18
El Tigre	75	400	29

[1] *Informe Económico Sobre Un Plan Ferroviario Nacional* (Caracas: Comisión Económica Ferroviaria Nacional, 1960), p. 189.

157

EVALUATION OF THE NEED FOR A BRIDGE OVER THE ORINOCO RIVER AT CIUDAD GUAYANA

Due to the magnitude of the investment involved, some special consideration should be given to the bridge over the Orinoco River at Ciudad Guayana. The justification for this bridge depends largely on the savings in user costs obtained as a result of its construction and thus on estimates of the traffic volumes that would use the bridge.

Traffic using the proposed bridge would be basically of two types: traffic destined for the areas around Maturín and Carúpano and traffic destined to the rest of the country, using the Los Barrancos-Templador road as an alternate to the route via El Tigre. As shown in Chapter Four, the need for this alternate route is not expected to arise before the 1975–1980 period. Thus construction of the bridge prior to this period would have to be based on user cost savings incurred by the first type of traffic alone.

Costs of crossing the river by ferry are estimated to range from Bs 24 to Bs 36 per truck. For automobiles, an average cost of Bs 4 is assumed. A crossing by ferry, however, would save approximately 5 kilometers of driving including access to the bridge, thereby reducing the user savings to some degree. Time savings also have an important influence on total user savings. Values of Bs 4 and Bs 14 per hour for cars and trucks, respectively, have been used in evaluating user benefits for the bridge at Ciudad Bolívar, whereas Bs 3 and Bs 4 per hour have been suggested in the case of the bridge over the Caroní.[1] For these figures the range of user cost savings for automobiles and trucks has been summarized in Table G.1. An equivalent

Table G.1. A Summary of Estimated User Cost Savings for the Proposed Bridge over the Orinoco at Ciudad Guayana

Items	Costs in Bolivars[1]	
	Low	High
Trucks		
Savings in Ferry Costs	24.0	36.0
Time Savings (0.5 hour)	2.0	7.0
Subtotal	26.0	43.0
Additional Operating Costs (5 km)	3.5	3.5
Net Truck Savings	22.5	39.5
Automobiles		
Savings in Ferry Costs	4.0	4.0
Time Savings (0.5 hour)	1.5	2.0
Subtotal	5.5	6.0
Additional Operating Costs (5 km)	0.8	0.8
Net Automobile Savings	4.7	5.2
Equivalent Savings per Truck Assuming Truck Traffic is 25% of Total	36.6	55.1

[1] *1959 prices.*

user saving per truck has also been indicated based on a traffic composition of 25% trucks, 75% automobiles.

On the basis of these user cost savings, traffic volumes at which annual savings are equivalent to annual bridge costs can be calculated as shown in Table G.2.

[1] Memo from Sergio Sánchez Naranjo to Roberto Alamo Blanco, Corporación Venezolana de Guayana, dated 11 May 1961.

159

Table G.2. Calculation of Break-Even Truck Traffic for the Proposed Bridge over the Orinoco River at Ciudad Guayana

Items	Interest Rate	
	8%	10%
Initial Bridge Cost in Bs	138,500,000	138,500,000
Annual Costs of Amortization at 35-year life in Bs	11,950,000	14,300,000
Annual Maintenance Costs in Bs	420,000	420,000
Total Annual Cost	12,370,000	14,720,000
Break-even Truck Volume in Trucks per Day		
at 36.6 Bs/Truck	920	1,100
at 55.1 Bs/Truck	610	730

When compared to the daily truck volumes estimated for Maturín previously (Table 4.7), the break-even volumes shown in Table G.2 indicate that the proposed bridge would not be justified on the basis of savings in user costs alone. For the high estimates of user savings and lower rate of interest, predicted daily truck traffic (120 trucks per day) is only about 20% of the break-even volume using high production targets. Even if bridge construction costs were to be reduced by one-half, traffic volumes would still be too low to justify construction of the bridge on the basis of the first type of traffic mentioned previously.

When diverted traffic is introduced, justification for the bridge improves considerably. If diverted traffic amounts to 50% of total traffic estimated to use an alternative four-lane El Tigre road, total daily truck traffic using the proposed bridge would reach about 800 trucks per day by 1980. This traffic diversion, however, would probably not occur before the capacity of the two-lane road to El Tigre is reached, estimated previously to occur between 1975 and 1980.

On the basis of high production targets for the Guayana region the proposed bridge across the Orinoco at Ciudad Guayana would, therefore, be required sometime during the 1975–1980 period. Allowing a lead time for construction of 5 years, a more detailed evaluation of the bridge should be made during the period 1970–1972. Revised traffic estimates could be made by comparing actual traffic volumes and levels of production at that time with those estimated for the same period.

SELECTED BIBLIOGRAPHY

Abramian, Pascual A. La Siderurgica Nacional y el Problema de Los Transportes de las Matérias Primas y Acabados. Caracas: Comisión Económica Ferroviaria Nacional, 1959.

Adler, Hans A. "Economic Evaluation of Transport Projects." In *Transport Investment and Economic Development*, edited by Gary Fromm. Washington: The Brookings Institution, 1965.

The Asphalt Handbook. College Park, Maryland: Asphalt Institute, 1961.

Baker, Robert F., and Emmett H. Karrer. *A Study of the Relationship of Pavement Cost to Vehicle Weight*, Bulletin 161, Engineering Experiment Station. Columbus: Ohio State University, 1956.

Baker, Robert F., Robert Chieruzzi, and Richard W. Bletzacker. *Highway Costs and the Relationship to Vehicle Size*. Engineering Experiment Station. Bulletin 168. Columbus: Ohio State University, 1958.

Beakey, John. *The Effect of Highway Design on Vehicle Speed and Fuel Consumption*. Technical Bulletin No. 5. Salem: Oregon State Highway Commission, 1937.

Beakey, John, and F. B. Crandall. *The Effect of Surface Type, Alignment and Traffic Congestion on Vehicular Fuel Consumption*. Technical Bulletin No. 17. Salem: Oregon State Highway Commission, 1944.

Bhagat, D. H. "Adequacy Assessment of Highways," *Journal of the Indian Roads Congress, XXII*, 1 (November, 1958), pp. 117–160.

Bhagat, D. G. "Regional Concept for Highway Planning: The Web and Lattice Pattern," *Journal of the Indian Roads Congress, XXIV*, 4 (January, 1960), pp. 629–666.

Bos, H. C., and L. M. Koyek. "The Appraisal of Investments in Transportation Projects; A Practical Example." *Review of Economics and Statistics, XLIII*, 1 (February, 1961), pp. 13–20.

Bourrières, Paul. *L'Economie des Transports dans les Programmes de Développement*. Paris: Presses Universitaires de France, 1961.

Brown, Robert Tennant. "Programming Investments in Transport. The Chilean Experience." (Unpublished Ph.D. thesis in Economics deposited in Harvard College Library, 1961).

Bulkley, G. V. O. *Transport Administration in Tropical Dependencies.* London, 1946.

Campbell, J. R. *Development of Roads in the Sudan.* United Nations Report No. TAA/SUD/2, 30 September 1957.

Capital Intensity and Costs in Earth Moving Operations, Industrialization and Productivity. Bulletin No. 3, United Nations Department of Economic and Social Affairs (March, 1960).

Capital Intensity in Heavy Engineering Construction, Industrialization and Productivity. Bulletin No. 1, United Nations Department of Economic and Social Affairs (April, 1958).

Capital Intensity in Industry in Underdeveloped Countries, Industrialization and Productivity. Bulletin No. 1, United Nations Department of Economic and Social Affairs (April, 1958).

Casey, Ralph E. "The Maritime Industry and its Problems" in *U.S. Transportation, Resources, Performance, and Problems.* Publication 841–S. Washington: National Academy of Sciences, 1961.

Chenery, Hollis B. "Engineering Production Functions," *Quarterly Journal of Economics, LXIII,* 4 (November, 1949).

Comisión de Normas, *Normas para el Proyecto de Carreteras.* Caracas: Ministerio de Obras Públicas, 1962.

Dabasi-Schweng, Lorand. *Food and the Industrial Development of the Guayana.* Caracas: Corporación Venezolana de Guayana (C.V.G.) Joint Center-Guayana Project, 5 December 1962. File No. B–32. (Mimeographed.)

Daftary, N. D., and M. K. Ganguli. "Road Transport Operation Cost on Various Types of Surfaces," *Journal of the Indian Roads Congress, XXIV,* 3 (December, 1959), pp. 517–542.

Dawson, R. F. F. *An Analysis of the Cost of Road Improvement Schemes.* Road Research Technical Paper No. 50. London: Her Majesty's Stationery Office, 1961.

de Sola, Oswaldo. "Necesidad de Una Definición Mecánica de las Rocas Para los Estúdios Geológicos de Carreteras," *Boletín de Mecánica del Suelo e Ingeniería de Fundaciones.* (Caracas, March, 1962).

"Dimensions and Weights of Road-Design Vehicles," *Journal of the Indian Roads Congress, XVII,* 2 (December, 1953), pp. 246–249.

Dubnie, Amil. *Transportation of Minerals in Northern Canada.* Mineral Information Bulletin MR–50. Ottawa: Queen's Printer, 1961.

Eckaus, R. S. "Choice of Technology," *The Economic Weekly Annual* (February 4, 1961) (India), pp. 147–202.

Eckaus, R. S. "Technological Change in the Less Developed Areas," *Development of the Emerging Countries, An Agenda for Research.* Washington: The Brookings Institute, 1962.

Economics of Asphalt and Concrete for Highway Construction. Menlo Park, California: Stanford Research Institute, 1961.

Elementos Para Una Politica de Desarrollo de la Industria Automotriz en Venezuela. Report to the Comisión Economica del Consejo de Ministros. Caracas: Oficina Central de Coordinación y Planificación, 1962.

Ferrocarril Guanta-Naricual, Informe. Caracas: Comisión Económica Ferroviaria Nacional, 1959.

Fischman, Leonard. *Notes on the Domestic and Export Markets for Certain Selected Materials.* File D–14. Caracas: C.V.G., Joint Center-Guayana Project, 16 June 1962. (Mimeographed.)

Friedmann, John. *Economic Growth and Urban Structure in Venezuela; Towards a Dynamic Theory of Spatial Organization.* Caracas: C.V.G., Joint Center-Guayana Project, 12 November 1962. (Mimeographed.) (Paper presented at the First Latin American Regional Science Congress, Caracas, Venezuela, November 12–14, 1962).

Fromm, Gary. Editor. *Transport Investment and Economic Development.* Washington: The Brookings Institution, 1965.

Fromm, Gary. "Design of the Transport Sector." In *Transport Investment and Economic Development,* edited by Gary Fromm. Washington: The Brookings Institution, 1965.

Galenson, Walter and Leibenstein, Harvey. "Investment Criteria, Productivity, and Economic Development," *Quarterly Journal of Economics, LXIX* (August, 1958).

Ganguli, M. K., and C. S. Anantapadmanabhan. "The Design of an Experiment to Assess the Cost of Operation of Motor Vehicles on Different Types of Roads," *Journal of the Indian Roads Congress, XX,* 2 (November, 1955).

Ganz, Alexander. *Preliminary Perspectives on the Role of the Guayana Region in the Economic Development of Venezuela.* File B–6. Caracas: C.V.G., Joint Center-Guayana Project, 26 March 1962. (Mimeographed.)

Ganz, Alexander. *World Demand for Present and Potential Guayana Region Minerals, Metals, Machinery, and Chemical Fertilizer Products; and Rest-of-Venezuela Demand for Guayana Region Metals and Machinery Products 1960–61, 1961–65–70–80–2000,* File B–14. Caracas: C.V.G., Joint Center-Guayana Project, 7 May 1962. (Mimeographed.)

Ganz, Alexander. *Regional Planning as a Key to the Present Stage of Economic Development of Latin America; The Case of the Guayana Region, A Frontier Region.* Paper presented at the First Latin American Regional Science Congress. Caracas, November 12–14, 1962.

Gillette, Halbert Powers. *Economics of Road Construction.* New York: Engineering News Publishing Co., 1906.

Gonzalez Lander, José O. "Highway Design-Cost Relationship." Unpublished S.M. thesis, Department of Civil Engineering, M.I.T., August, 1962.

Grant, Eugene L., and W. Grant Ireson. *Principles of Engineering Economy.* New York: Ronald Press, 1960.

Grossman, William L. *Fundamentals of Transportation.* New York: Simmons-Boardman Publishing Corporation, 1959.

Hawkins, E. K. *Road Transport in Nigeria, A Study of African Enterprise.* London: Oxford University Press, 1958, 97 pp.

Hawkins, E. K. *Roads and Road Transport in an Underdeveloped Country, A Case Study of Uganda.* London: Her Majesty's Stationery Office, 1962, 254 pp.

Hay, William H. *An Introduction to Transportation Engineering.* New York: John Wiley & Sons, Inc., 1961.

Heflebower, Richard B. "Characteristics of Transport Modes." In *Transport Investment and Economic Development,* edited by Gary Fromm. Washington: The Brookings Institution, 1965.

Hewes, Lawrence Ilsley. *American Highway Practice,* Volume I. New York: John Wiley & Sons, Inc., 1942.

Highway Research Board. *Line-Haul Trucking Costs in Relation to Vehicle Gross Weights.* Bulletin 301. Washington: National Academy of Sciences, 1961.

Hill, M. F. *Permanent Way. The Story of the Kenya and Uganda Railway.* Nairobi, 1949.

Hirschman, Albert O. *The Strategy of Economic Development.* New Haven, Conn.: Yale University Press, 1961.

Hirshleifer, Jack, James C. DeHaven, and Jerome W. Milliman. *Water Supply, Economics, Technology and Policy.* Chicago: University of Chicago Press, 1960.

Holmstrom, J. Edwin. *Railways and Roads in Pioneer Development Overseas: A Study of Their Comparative Economics.* London: P. S. King and Son, Ltd., 1934.

Hunter, Holland. "Resources, Transportation, and Economic Development," in *Natural Resources and Economic Growth.* Washington: Resources for the Future, 1960.

Informe de la Comisión Para el Estudio del Funcionamiento de los Puertos de Venezuela. Caracas: Colegio de Ingenieros de Venezuela, 7 April 1960. (Mimeographed.)

Informe Económico Sobre Un Plan Ferroviario Nacional. Caracas: Comisión Económica Ferroviaria Nacional, 1960.

International Bank for Reconstruction and Development, *The Economic Development of British Guiana.* Baltimore: The Johns Hopkins Press, 1953.

165

International Bank for Reconstruction and Development, *The World Bank in Africa*. Washington, 1961.

International Bank for Reconstruction and Development, *The World Bank in Asia*. Washington, 1960.

International Bank for Reconstruction and Development, *The Economic Development of Venezuela*. Baltimore: The Johns Hopkins Press, 1960.

International Bank for Reconstruction and Development, and the International Development Association, *The World Bank and IDA in the Americas*. Washington, 1962.

Isard, Walter, et al. *Methods of Regional Analysis: An Introduction to Regional Science*. New York: John Wiley & Sons, Inc., 1960.

Kimble, George H. T. *Tropical Africa, Land and Livelihood*, Vol. 1, Abridged Edition. Garden City, N.Y.: Doubleday & Company, Inc., 1962.

Kotler, Philip. A review of A. K. Sen. *Choice of Techniques: An Aspect of the Theory of Planned Economic Development*. Oxford: Basil Blackwell, 1960, 122 pp. In *Economic Development and Cultural Change*, X, 3, April 1962.

Kuhn, Tillo E. "Economic Analyses for Highway Improvements in Developing Countries." Paper presented at the Ninth Pan American Highway Congress, Washington, D.C., May 6–18, 1963. Reprint No. 126, Institute of Transportation and Traffic Engineering, University of California.

Kuhn, Tillo E., and Michael Nelson. "Economic Investment and Transport Investment Planning: A Case Study in Honduras." Paper presented at the Ninth Pan American Highway Congress, Washington, D.C., May 6–18, 1963. Reprint No. 127, Institute of Transportation and Traffic Engineering, University of California.

Lang, A. S., and D. H. Robbins. "A New Technique for Predicting Vehicle Operating Cost," in *Operational Effects of Design and Traffic Engineering*. Washington: Highway Research Board, 1962. Bulletin 308.

Lang, A. S., P. O. Roberts, and D. H. Robbins. "An Evaluation of Techniques for Highway User Cost Computation," in *Studies in Highway Engineering Economy*. Washington: Highway Research Board, 1962. Bulletin 320.

Lefeber, Louis. *Allocation in Space. Production, Transport and Industrial Location*. Amsterdam: North Holland Publishing Co., 1958.

Lefeber, Louis. "On the Interaction of Transportation and Regional Development," *Transportation Design Considerations*. Publication 841. Washington: National Academy of Sciences, National Research Council, 1961.

Lefeber, Louis. *Economic Development and Regional Growth.* Paper presented at a conference on Transportation Economics. New York: National Bureau of Economic Research Inc., 26 April 1963. (Mimeographed.)

Lewis, W. A. *Further Studies in the Compaction of Soil and the Performance of Compaction Plant,* Road Research Technical Paper 33. London: Her Majesty's Stationery Office, 1954.

Lewis, W. A. *Investigation of the Performance of Pneumatic Tyred Rollers in the Compaction of Soil,* Road Research Technical Paper 45. London: Her Majesty's Stationery Office, 1959.

Lewis, W. A., and A. W. Parsons, The Performance of Compaction Plant in the Compaction of Two Types of Granular Base Material, Road Research Technical Paper 53. London: Her Majesty's Stationery Office, 1961.

Maass, Arthur, et al. Design of Water Resource Systems. Cambridge: Harvard University Press, 1962.

Madigan-Hyland South American Corporation. *Economic Feasibility of Magdalena Valley Railroad Extension.* New York, 1954.

Madigan-Hyland South American Corporation. *Rehabilitation of National Railroads of Colombia.* New York, 1956.

Madigan-Hyland South American Corporation. *Comparative Studies for Transfer of Railroad Freight Between Barranquilla and Cienaga.* New York, 1961.

Manheim, Marvin L. "Data Accuracy in Route Location," *Traffic Quarterly,* XV, 1 (January, 1961), pp. 153–178.

Martin, Brian V., and Charles B. Warden. "Transportation Planning in Developing Countries," *Traffic Quarterly,* XXIX, 1, (January, 1965), pp. 59–75.

McCullough, C. B., and J. Beakey, The Economics of Highway Planning. Technical Bulletin No. 7. Salem: Oregon State Highway Commission, September, 1937.

Mehra, S. R., and H. L. Uppal. "The Importance of Subgrade Compaction in the Economic Design of Flexible Pavements," *Journal of the Indian Roads Congress,* XXII, 3 (December, 1957), pp. 425–454.

Mehra, S. R., C. G. Swaminathan, and V. R. Vaish. "Scientific Design and Laying of a Bituminous Carpet on a National Highway," *Journal of the Indian Roads Congress,* XXIV, 3 (December, 1959), pp. 475–516.

Meyer, John R., et al. *The Economics of Competition in the Transportation Industries.* Cambridge, Mass.: Harvard University Press, 1959.

Miller, C. L., A. S. Lang, and D. H. Robbins. *Vehicle Simulation and Operating Cost System.* Cambridge: Department of Civil Engineering, Massachusetts Institute of Technology, 1961. Publication 142.

Miller, C. L., A. S. Lang, and D. H. Robbins. *Research Report on the Vehicle Simulation and Operating Cost System.* Cambridge: Department of Civil Engineering, Massachusetts Institute of Technology, 1961. Publication 143.

Miller-Warden-Western, Dorsch-Gehrman, *Economic and Technical Soundness Analysis of Four Transportation Projects in Venezuela.* Raleigh, N.C.: Miller Warden Associates, November 12, 1962.

Moyer, R. A., and Robley Winnfrey. *Cost of Operating Rural-Mail-Carrier Motor Vehicles on Pavement, Gravel, and Earth.* Bulletin 143. Ames, Iowa: Iowa Engineering Experiment Station, 1939.

Moyer, R. A. *Effect of Vehicle Operating Costs on the Selection of Road Surface.* Proceedings of the 27th Annual Highway Conference. University of Michigan Official Publications, 1941.

Moyer, R. A., and G. L. Tesdell. *Tire Wear and Cost on Selected Roadway Surfaces.* Bulletin 161. Ames, Iowa: Iowa State College Engineering Experiment Station, 1945.

Munby, D. L. "Investment in Road and Rail Transport," *Institute of Transport Journal,* 29, 9 (March, 1962), pp. 271–279.

Naciones Unidas. *Analysis y Projecciones del Desarrollo Económico,* III El Desarrollo Económico de Colombia (E/CN.12/365/Rev. 1) Mexico, 1957.

Nelson, James R. "Pricing Transport Services." In *Transport Investment and Economic Development,* edited by Gary Fromm. Washington: The Brookings Institution, 1965.

Odier, Lionel. *The Economic Benefits of Road Construction and Improvements.* Translated from the French, *Les Intérêts Economiques des Travaux Routiers.* Paris: French Ministry of Public Works, undated (ca. 1964).

Oficina Central de Coordinación y Planificación, *Elementos Para Una Política de Desarrollo de la Industria Automotríz en Venezuela,* Report to the Comisión Económica del Consejo de Ministros (Caracas, 1962).

Oglesby, Clarkson H., and Lawrence I. Hewes, *Highway Engineering,* Second Edition. New York: John Wiley & Sons, Inc., 1964.

Okita, Saburo. "Choice of Techniques," *Industrialization and Productivity.* Bulletin No. 4. United Nations Department of Social and Economic Affairs. April, 1961.

Owen, Wilfred. *Strategy for Mobility.* Washington: The Brookings Institution, 1964.

Parsons, Brinckerhoff, Quade and Douglas. *Plan for Improvements in National Transportation.* Bogota: Ministry of Public Works, Republic of Colombia, December 1961.

Perazich, George. *Preliminary Program of Potential Industrial Development Projects for the Guayana Region.* Caracas: C.V.G., Joint Center-Guayana Project, 26 March 1962. (Mimeographed).

Permanent International Association of Road Congresses. *Sixth Congress, Washington, 1930, Reports.* Washington: U.S. Government Printing Office, 1930.

Permanent International Association of Road Congresses, *Sixth International Road Congress, Proceedings, Washington, 1930.* Washington: U.S. Government Printing Office, 1931.

Phillips, Joseph D. *Consumption Estimates for Ciudad Guayana 1970 and 1980.* Caracas: C.V.G., Joint Center-Guayana Project, 20 November 1962. (Mimeographed.)

Policy on Maintenance of Roadway Surfaces. Washington: American Association of State Highway Officials (AASHO), 1948.

Policy on Maintenance of Shoulders, Road Approaches and Sidewalks. Washington: American Association of State Highway Officials (AASHO), 1949.

Policy on Geometric Design of Rural Highways. Washington: American Association of State Highway Officials (AASHO), 1949.

Pool, A. G. "The Subsidizing of Public Transport," *Journal of the Institute of Transport,* 28, 12 (September, 1960), pp. 365–369.

Rangel, José Antonio, Lawrence Bridge, and Gordon A. Marker, *The Guayana Development Program,* draft prepared for the *Plan de la Nación,* 1965–1968, Corporación Venezolana de Guayana, División de Planificación Sector Económico, March 1965, File No. B–80.

Rao, N. Mohan. "Design of Roads for Bullock-Cart Traffic," Road Research Bulletin No. 6. The Indian Roads Congress, New Delhi, 1959.

Reynolds, D. J. *The Effect cf Road Conditions on Fuel Consumption.* Harmondsworth, England: Road Research Laboratory, 1956. (Unpublished).

Reynolds, D. J. *The Assessment of Priority for Road Improvements.* Road Research Technical Paper No. 48. London: Her Majesty's Stationery Office, 1960.

Road Research Laboratory. *The Investigation of Road Foundation Failures.* London: Her Majesty's Stationery Office, 1950.

Road Research Laboratory. *Concrete Roads: Design and Construction.* London: Her Majesty's Stationery Office, 1955.

Road Research Laboratory, *Road Research 1959.* London: Her Majesty's Stationery Office, 1960.

Road User Benefit Analyses for Highway Improvements. Washington: American Association of State Highway Officials, 1960.

Roberts, Merrill J. "Some Aspects of Motor Carrier Costs: Firm Size, Efficiency and Financial Health," *Land Economics, 32,* 3 (August, 1956).

Roberts, Paul O., and A. Villaveces. *Digital Terrain Model (DTM) Design System.* Research Report R62–6. Cambridge: Department of Civil Engineering, Massachusetts Institute of Technology, 1961.

Roberts, Paul O., and John H. Suhrbier. *Location Analysis: A Computer-Based Approach.* Paper P63–17. Cambridge: Department of Civil Engineering, Massachusetts Institute of Technology, 1963.

"The Role of Road Transport in the National Economy," *Journal of the Indian Roads Congress, XVIII,* 3 (January, 1954), pp. 453–458.

Saal, Carl. *Tire and Gasoline Consumption in Motor Truck Operations as Affected by the Weight and Power of Vehicles and the Rise and Fall in Highways.* Research Report No. 9–A. Washington: Highway Research Board, 1950.

Sain, Kanwar and L. K. Rao, *Report on the Recent River Valley Projects in China.* New Delhi: Government of India, Central Water and Power Commission, 1955.

Sánchez Naranjo, Sergio. *El Desarrollo Económico de la Región Suroriental y Los Transportes.* Caracas: C.V.G., División de Estúdios, Planificación y Investigación, January, 1962.

Sen, Amartya Kumar. *Choice of Techniques. An Aspect of the Theory of Planned Economic Development.* Oxford: Basil Blackwell, 1960.

Smith, N. D. S. *A Pilot Study in Uganda of the Effects Upon Economic Development of the Construction of Feeder Roads.* Harmondsworth, England: Road Research Laboratory, February, 1959.

Specifications for Construction, Bituminous Surfacing. Washington: AASHO, 1949.

Srinivasan, Thirukodikoval N. "Investment Criteria and Choice of Techniques," *Yale Economic Essays, II,* 1 (1962). (Also Cowles Foundation Paper No. 177.)

Srivastava, S. K. *Transport Development in India.* Ghaziabad: Deepak Publishing House, 1956.

Stringer, H. *Pioneer Railway Engineering.* London: H. F. and G. Witherby, 1923.

Subbaraju, Bh. and Dhir, M.P. "Economics of Highway Pavement Design," The Indian Roads Congress, Bulletin No. 6 (December, 1959).

Taaffe, Robert. *Rail Transportation and the Economic Development of Soviet Central Asia.* Chicago: University of Chicago Press, 1960.

Tinbergen, J. *On the Theory of Economic Policy.* Amsterdam: North Holland Publishing Company, 1955.

Tinbergen, J. *Economic Policy: Principles and Design.* Amsterdam: North Holland Publishing Company, 1956.

Tinbergen, Jan. "The Appraisal of Road Construction: Two Calculation Schemes," *Review of Economics and Statistics, XXXIX,* 3 (August, 1957).

Tinbergen, Jan. "Choice of Technology in Industrial Planning," *Industrialization and Productivity.* Bulletin No. 1. United Nations Department of Economic and Social Affairs (April, 1958).

Transportation, Vol. V, *Science, Technology, and Development.* United States Papers prepared for the United Nations Conference on the Application of Science and Technology for the Benefit of the Less Developed Areas. Washington: U.S. Government Printing Office, 1962–1963.

United Nations Economic Commission for Asia and the Far East. *Programming Techniques for Economic Development.* Bangkok: United Nations, 1960.

United Nations Economic Commission for Latin America. *Analysis and Projections of Economic Development. I. An Introduction to the Technique of Programming.* New York: United Nations Department of Economic and Social Affairs, 1955.

United Nations. *Manual on Economic Development Projects.* New York, 1958.

United States Congress. *Final Report on the Highway Cost Allocation Study.* House Document No. 54. Washington: U.S. Government Printing Office, 1961.

United States War Department. *Inspections and Preventive Maintenance Services for Buildings and Structures, Grounds, Roads and Pavements and Railroads.* Washington: U.S. Government Printing Office, 1946.

"Use of Models in Programming," *Industrialization and Productivity.* Bulletin No. 4. United Nations Department of Economic and Social Affairs (April, 1961).

Viner, Jacob. "Cost Curves and Supply Curves," in *Readings in Price Theory,* edited by George J. Stigler and Kenneth E. Boulding. Chicago: Richard D. Irwin Inc., 1952.

Walker, Gilbert. *Traffic and Transport in Nigeria. The Example of an Underdeveloped Tropical Territory.* London: Her Majesty's Stationery Office, 1959.

Warden, Katherine D. "Selected Bibliography: Transportation and Economic Development." in *Transport Investment and Economic Development,* edited by Gary Fromm. Washington: The Brookings Institution, 1965.

Weld, William Ernest. "India's Demand for Transportation." *Studies in History, Economics and Public Law, XC,* 2. New York: Columbia University, Longmans, Green and Company, Agents, 1920.

Wilson, George W. "On the Output Unit in Transportation," *Land Economics, XXXV,* 3 (August, 1959), pp. 266–276.

Winnfrey, Robley. "Highway Economics." in *Highway Engineering Handbook,* edited by Kenneth B. Woods. New York: McGraw Hill, 1960.

Wohl, Paul, and A. Albetreccia. *Road and Rail in 40 Countries.* London: Oxford University Press, 1935.

Wooltorton, F. L. D. *The Scientific Basis of Road Design.* London: Edward Arnold Ltd., 1954.

Wonders, William C. "Roads and Winter Roads in the MacKenzie Valley Area." Paper presented at the Annual Meeting, British Columbia Division, Canadian Association of Geographers, Vancouver, B.C. March 24, 1962.

Yoder, E. J. *Principles of Pavement Design.* New York: John Wiley & Sons, Inc., 1959.

INDEX

Page numbers in italics refer to key illustrations.

173